THE CONCISE
CARPENTERS

WISE PUBLICATIONS
LONDON/NEW YORK/PARIS/SYDNEY/COPENHAGEN/MADRID

EXCLUSIVE DISTRIBUTORS:
MUSIC SALES LIMITED
8/9 FRITH STREET,
LONDON W1V 5TZ, ENGLAND.
MUSIC SALES PTY LIMITED
120 ROTHSCHILD AVENUE,
ROSEBERY, NSW 2018,
AUSTRALIA.

ORDER NO. AM933196
ISBN 0-7119-5237-X
THIS BOOK © COPYRIGHT 1995 BY WISE PUBLICATIONS

COMPILED BY PETER EVANS
MUSIC ARRANGED AND PROCESSED BY BARNES MUSIC ENGRAVING
BOOK DESIGN BY PEARCE MARCHBANK, STUDIO TWENTY
QUARKED BY BEN MAY
PHOTOGRAPHS COURTESY OF REDFERNS

PRINTED IN THE UNITED KINGDOM BY
J.B. OFFSET PRINTERS (MARKS TEY) LIMITED, MARKS TEY, ESSEX.

YOUR GUARANTEE OF QUALITY...

AS PUBLISHERS, WE STRIVE TO PRODUCE EVERY BOOK TO THE
HIGHEST COMMERCIAL STANDARDS.
THE MUSIC HAS BEEN FRESHLY ENGRAVED AND THE BOOK HAS BEEN CAREFULLY DESIGNED
TO MINIMISE AWKWARD PAGE TURNS AND TO MAKE PLAYING FROM IT A REAL PLEASURE.
THROUGHOUT, THE PRINTING AND BINDING HAVE BEEN PLANNED TO ENSURE A STURDY,
ATTRACTIVE PUBLICATION WHICH SHOULD GIVE YEARS OF ENJOYMENT.
IF YOUR COPY FAILS TO MEET OUR HIGH STANDARDS, PLEASE INFORM US
AND WE WILL GLADLY REPLACE IT.

MUSIC SALES' COMPLETE CATALOGUE DESCRIBES THOUSANDS OF TITLES
AND IS AVAILABLE IN FULL COLOUR SECTIONS BY SUBJECT,
DIRECT FROM MUSIC SALES LIMITED.
PLEASE STATE YOUR AREAS OF INTEREST AND SEND
A CHEQUE/POSTAL ORDER FOR £1.50 FOR POSTAGE TO:
MUSIC SALES LIMITED, NEWMARKET ROAD,
BURY ST. EDMUNDS, SUFFOLK IP33 3YB.

IN BOTH 'THE LYRICS' AND 'THE MUSIC' SECTIONS
EACH SONG BEARS THE SAME NUMBER, AS LISTED BELOW...

1
A SONG FOR YOU

I've been so many places in my life and time,
I've sung a lot of songs, I've made some bad rhyme,
I've acted out my love in stages, with ten thousand
  people watching,
But we're alone now, and I'm singing this song for
  you.

I know your image of me is what I hope to be,
I've treated you unkindly, but darling, can't you see?
There's no-one more important to me, darling, can't
  you please see through me?
But we're alone now, and I'm singing this song for
  you.

You taught me precious secrets of a truth, withholding
  nothing,
You came out in front, and I was hiding,
But now I'm so much better,
And if my words don't come together,
Listen to the melody,
'cause my love is in there hiding, ooh.

I'll love you in a place where there's no space or time,
I'll love you, for in my life you are a friend of mine,
And when my life is over, remember when we were
  together,
We were alone, and I was singing this song for you.

You taught me precious secrets of a truth, withholding
  nothing,
You came out in front, and I was hiding,
But now I'm so much better,
And if my words don't come together,
Listen to the melody,
'cause my love is in there hiding, ooh.

I'll love you in a place where there's no space or time,
I'll love you, for in my life you are a friend of mine,
And when my life is over, remember when we were
  together,
We were alone, and I was singing this song for you.
We were alone, and I was singing this song for you.

2
ANOTHER SONG

The moon that rose, now descended,
And the love one shared now had ended,
And soon the day would come.
And when the day had come,
The light that fell at dawn was cold,
The warmth of you had gone.

A taste of loneliness cut through the earliness,
And, oh, the wind sang of you.
Softly they said
All my favourite dreams were dead,
Leaving a cloud
Of sadness in my head.

And though I'm buried in a sad song of the morning
  way,
I know the day will bring
Another song for me to sing,
But when the day had come,
The light that fell at dawn was cold,
The warmth of you had gone.

3
CAN'T SMILE
WITHOUT YOU

You know I can't smile without you,
I can't smile without you,
I can't laugh, and I can't walk,
I'm finding it hard even to talk,
And I feel sad when you're sad,
I feel glad when you're glad,
And you must know what I'm going through,
I just can't smile without you.

You came along, just like a song
You brightened my day.
Who'd believe you were part of a dream
That only seemed light years away?

And you know I can't smile without you,
I can't smile without you,
I can't laugh, and I can't walk,
I'm finding it hard even to talk,
And I feel sad when you're sad,
I feel glad when you're glad,
And you must know what I'm going through,
I just can't smile without you.

Some people say the happiest wave
Is something that's hard to find.
Into the new,
Leaving the old behind me,
And I feel sad when you're sad,
I feel glad when you're glad,
And you must know what I'm going through,
I just can't smile without you.

Into the new, leaving the old behind me,
And I feel sad when you're sad,
I feel glad when you're glad,
And you must know what I'm going through,
I just can't smile without you.

4
CRYSTAL LULLABY

Listen to the song he sings.
Can't you see his music brings her crystal sleep?
As her heavy eyelids fall,
He's taking her to where the dolls rule the world,
And in that land of make believe,
Is where he'll leave her sleeping,
Softly warm in a crystal lullaby.

He's weaving her a paper castle,
Where dancing clowns with tassels made of fur,
Welcome her into their world,
That lives inside the dreams of every little girl.
She's guarded by a brave tin soldier,
Sitting on her shoulder,
Taken there in a crystal lullaby.

Sometimes, when I listen to the velvet song,
That fills the summer afternoon,
Something deep within me sighs,
And wishes for the peaceful skies of long ago,
That wrapped my cares in silver air,
And carried them away,
Leaving me, and a crystal lullaby.

That wrapped my cares in silver air,
And carried them away,
Leaving me, and a crystal lullaby.

5
DO YOU KNOW THE WAY TO SAN JOSE

Do you know the way to San Jose?
I've been away so long,
I may go wrong, and lose my way.
Do you know the way to San Jose?
I'm going back to find
Some peace of mind in San Jose.

L.A. is a great big freeway,
Put a hundred down, and buy a car,
In a week, maybe two, they'll make you a star,
Weeks turn into years, how quick they pass,
And all the stars that never were
Are parking cars, and pumping gas.

You can really breathe in San Jose,
They've got a lot of space,
There'll be a place where I can stay.
I was born and raised in San Jose,
I'm going back to find
Some peace of mind in San Jose.

Fame and fortune is a big magnet,
It can pull you far away from home,
With a dream in your heart, you're never alone,
Dreams turn into dust, and blow away,
And there you are without a friend,
Now pack the car and ride away.

I've got lots of friends in San Jose.
Can't wait to get back to San Jose.
Do you know the way to San Jose?

6
BREAKING UP IS HARD TO DO

Come-a come-a down do-be do dum down,
Come-a come-a down do-be do dum down,
Come-a come-a down do-be do dum down,
Breaking up is hard to do.

Don't take your love away from me,
Don't you leave my heart in misery,
If you go then I'll be blue,
'Cause breaking up is hard to do.

Remember when you held me tight,
And you kissed me all through the night?
Think of all that we've been through,
'cause breaking up is hard to do.

They say that breaking up is hard to do,
Now I know, I know that it's true.
Don't say that this is the end,
Instead of breaking up, I wish that we were
  making up again.

I beg of you, don't say goodbye.
Can't we give our love another try?
Come on, baby, let's start anew,
'cause breaking up is hard to do.

I beg of you, don't say goodbye.
Can't we give our love another try?
Come on, baby, let's start anew,
'cause breaking up is hard to do,
Yeah, breaking up is hard to do.

Do do do down do-be do dum down,
Come-a come-a down do-be do dum down.

Come-a come-a down do-be do dum down,
Come-a come-a down do-be do dum down.

7
DON'T CRY FOR ME ARGENTINA

It won't be easy,
You'll think it strange,
When I try to explain how I feel,
That I still need your love after all that I've done.
You won't believe me,
All you will see is a girl you once knew,
Although she's dressed up to the nines,
At sixes and sevens with you.

I had to let it happen,
I had to change,
Couldn't stay all my life down at heel,
Looking down out the window, staying out of the sun.
So, I chose freedom,
Running around trying everything new,
But nothing impressed me at all.
I never expected it to.

Don't cry for me Argentina,
The truth is I never left you.
All through my wild days, my mad existence,
I kept my promise, don't keep your distance.

And as for fortune,
And as for fame,
I never invited them in,
Though it seemed to the world they were all I desired.
They are illusions,
They're not the solutions they promise to be.
The answer was here all the time.
I love you, and hope you love me.

Don't cry for me Argentina,
The truth is I never left you.
All through my wild days, my mad existence,
I kept my promise, don't keep your distance.

Don't cry for me Argentina,
The truth is I never left you.
All through my wild days, my mad existence,
I kept my promise, don't keep your distance.
Have I said too much?
There's nothing more I can think of to say to you,
But all you have to do is look at me,
To know that every word is true.

8
FOR ALL WE KNOW

Love, look at the two of us,
Strangers in many ways.
We've got a lifetime to share, so much to say,
And as we go from day to day,
I'll feel you close to me,
But time alone will tell.
Let's take a lifetime to say, 'I knew you well,'
For only time will tell us so,
And love may grow,
For all we know.

Love, look at the two of us,
Strangers in many ways.
Let's take a lifetime to say, 'I knew you well,'
For only time will tell us so,
And love may grow,
For all we know.

9
GOODBYE TO LOVE

I'll say goodbye to love,
No one ever cared if I should live or die.
Time and time again, the chance for love has
    passed me by,
And all I know of love is how to live without it,
I just can't seem to find it.
So I've made my mind up, I must live my life alone,
And though it's not the easy way,
I guess I've always known.

I'd say goodbye to love,
There are no tomorrows for this heart of mine.
Surely, time will lose these bitter memories,
And I'll find that there is someone to believe in,
    and to live for,
Something I could live for.
All the years of useless search have finally reached
    an end,
Loneliness and empty days
Will be my only friend.

From this day love is forgotten,
I'll go on as best I can.

What lies in the future is a mystery to us all,
No one can predict the wheel of fortune as it falls.
There may come a time when I will see that I've
    been wrong,
But for now, this is my song, and it's goodbye to love.
I'll say goodbye to love. Ah, ah.

10
HURTING EACH OTHER

No one in the world ever had a love as sweet as
    my love,
For nowhere in the world could there be a boy as
    true as you, love.
All my love, I give gladly to you, all your love,
    you give gladly to me.
Tell me why then, why should it be that we go on
    hurting each other?
We go on hurting each other, making each other cry,
Hurting each other, without ever knowing why.

Closer than the leaves on a weepin' willow, baby,
    we are,
Closer dear, are we, than the simple letters A and B
    are.
All my life, I could love only you, all your life,
    you could love only me.
Tell me why then, why should it be that we go on
    hurting each other?
We go on hurting each other, making each other cry,
Hurting each other, without ever knowing why.

Can't we stop hurting each other?
Can't we stop hurting each other, making each
    other cry,
Breaking each other's heart, tearing each other apart?

11
I WON'T LAST A DAY
WITHOUT YOU

Day after day, I must face a world of strangers,
Where I don't belong, I'm not that strong.
It's nice to know that there's someone I can turn to,
Who will always care, you're always there.

When there's no getting over that rainbow,
When my smallest of dreams won't come true,
I can take all the madness the world has to give,
But I won't last a day without you.

So many times, when the city seems to be
Without a friendly face, a lonely place.
It's nice to know that you'll be there if I need you,
And you'll always smile, it's all worthwhile.

When there's no getting over that rainbow,
When my smallest of dreams won't come true,
I can take all the madness the world has to give,
But I won't last a day without you.

Touch me, and I end up singing,
Troubles seem to up and disappear.
You touch me with the love you're bringing,
I can't really lose when you're near, when you're near,
  my love.

If all my friends have forgotten half their promises,
They're not unkind, just hard to find.
One look at you, and I know that I could learn to love
Without the rest, I found the best.

When there's no getting over that rainbow,
When my smallest of dreams won't come true,
I can take all the madness the world has to give,
But I won't last a day without you.

When there's no getting over that rainbow,
When my smallest of dreams won't come true,
I can take all the madness the world has to give,
But I won't last a day without you.

12
I NEED TO BE IN LOVE

The hardest thing I've ever done
Is keep believing there's someone in this crazy world
  for me.
The way that people come and go through temporary
  lives,
My chance could come and I might never know.

I used to say, 'No promises, let's keep it simple,'
But freedom only helps you say goodbye.
It took a while for me to learn that nothing comes
  for free,
The price I've paid is high enough for me.

I know I need to be in love,
I know I've wasted too much time,
I know I ask perfection of a quite imperfect world,
And fool enough to think that's what I'll find.

So, here I am with pockets full of good intentions,
But none of them will comfort me tonight.
I'm wide awake at four a.m. without a friend in sight,
I'm hanging on a hoop, but I'm all right.

I know I need to be in love,
I know I've wasted too much time,
I know I ask perfection of a quite imperfect world,
And fool enough to think that's what I'll find.

I know I need to be in love,
I know I've wasted too much time,
I know I ask perfection of a quite imperfect world,
And fool enough to think that's what I'll find.

13
I'LL NEVER FALL IN LOVE AGAIN

Here to remind you, here to remind you,
Here to remind you, here to remind you.

What do you get when you fall in love?
A guy with a pin to burst your bubble,
That's what you get for all your trouble,
I'll never fall in love again, I'll never fall in love again.

What do you get when you kiss a guy?
You get enough germs to catch pneumonia.
If you do, he'll never phone ya,
I'll never fall in love again, I'll never fall in love again.

Don't tell me what it's all about,
'cause I've been there, and I'm glad I'm out,
Out of those chains, those chains that bind you.
That is why I'm here to remind you.

What do you get when you fall in love?
You get enough tears to fill an ocean.
That's what you get for your devotion,
I'll never fall in love again, I'll never fall in love again.

Don't tell me what it's all about,
'cause I've been there, and I'm glad I'm out,
Out of those chains, those chains that bind you.
That is why I'm here to remind you, here to remind
   you.

What do you get when you fall in love?
You only get lies and pain, and sorrow.
So, for at least until tomorrow,
I'll never fall in love again, I'll never fall in love again.

14
IT'S GOING TO TAKE SOME TIME

It's going to take some time this time,
To get myself in shape.
I really fell out of line this time,
I really missed the gate.
The birds on the telephone line, next time,
Are crying out to me, next time,
And I won't be so blind next time,
And I'll find some harmony.

But it's going to take some time this time,
And I can't make demands,
But like the young trees in the winter time,
I'll learn how to bend.
After all the tears we spent,
How could we make amends?
So it's one more round for experience,
And I'm on the road again.

And it's going to take some time this time,
And I can't make demands.
I'll learn how to bend.

It's going to take some time this time,
No matter what I play,
But like the young trees in the winter time,
I'll learn how to bend.
After all the tears we've spent,
How could I make amends?
So it's one more round for experience,
And I'm on the road again,
And it's going to take some time this time.

15
JAMBALAYA
(ON THE BAYOU)

Goodbye Joe, he gotta go, me oh my oh,
He gotta go pole the pirogue down the bayou.
His Yvonne, the sweetest one, me oh my oh,
Son of a gun, we'll have big fun on the bayou.

Thibodeaux, Fountaineaux, the place is buzzin',
Kinfolk come to see Yvonne by the dozen.
Dressed in style, they go hog-wild, me oh my oh,
Son of a gun, we'll have big fun on the bayou.

Jambalaya, and a crawfish pie, and fillet gumbo,
For tonight I'm gonna see my ma cher amio,
Pick guitar, fill fruit jar, and be gay-o,
Son of a gun, we'll have big fun on the bayou.

Settle down, far from town, get him a pirogue,
And he'll catch all the fish in the bayou.
Swap his mon to buy Yvonne what she need-o,
Son of a gun, we'll have big fun on the bayou.

Jambalaya, and a crawfish pie, and fillet gumbo,
For tonight I'm gonna see my ma cher amio,
Pick guitar, fill fruit jar, and be gay-o,
Son of a gun, we'll have big fun on the bayou.

Jambalaya, and a crawfish pie, and fillet gumbo,
For tonight I'm gonna see my ma cher amio,
Pick guitar, fill fruit jar, and be gay-o,
Son of a gun, we'll have big fun on the bayou.

Jambalaya, and a crawfish pie, and fillet gumbo,
For tonight I'm gonna see my ma cher amio,
Pick guitar, fill fruit jar, and be gay-o,
Son of a gun, we'll have big fun on the bayou.

Jambalaya, and a crawfish pie, and fillet gumbo,
For tonight I'm gonna see my ma cher amio,
Pick guitar, fill fruit jar, and be gay-o,
Son of a gun, we'll have big fun on the bayou.

16
LET ME BE THE ONE

Some sleepless night,
If you should find yourself alone,
Let me be the one you run to,
Let me be the one you come to
When you need someone to turn to,
Let me be the one.

To set things right,
When this old world's turned upside down,
Let me be the one you run to,
Let me be the one you come to
When you need someone to turn to,
Let me be the one.

For love and understanding,
To find a quiet place,
For silent understanding,
A loving touch.

Come to me when things go wrong,
And there's no love to light the way,
Let me be the one you run to,
Let me be the one you come to
When you need someone to turn to,
Let me be the one.

Let me be the one you run to,
Let me be the one you come to
When you need someone to turn to.

17
PLEASE MR POSTMAN

Stop! Whoah yes, wait a minute Mister Postman, wait!
Wait Mister Postman.
Please Mister Postman, look and see,
If there's a letter in your bag for me.
Why's it taking such a long time,
For me to hear from that boy of mine?

There must be some word today,
From my boyfriend so far away.
Please Mister Postman, look and see,
If there's a letter, a letter for me.
I've been standing here waiting, Mister Postman,
So patiently, for just a card, or just a letter,
Saying he's returning home to me.

Please Mister Postman, look and see,
If there's a letter in your bag for me.
Why's it taking such a long time,
For me to hear from that boy of mine?

So many days you passed me by,
See the tears standing in my eyes.
You didn't stop to make me feel better,
But even me, I got her a letter.

Please Mister Postman, look and see,
If there's a letter in your bag for me,
Why's it taking such a long time,
Such a long time?

Why don't you check it and see,
One more time for me?
You got to wait a minute, wait a minute,
Wait a minute, wait a minute,
Mister Postman, look and see,
Come on deliver the letter,
The sooner the better.

Mister Postman. Ah, ah.

18
RAINY DAYS AND MONDAYS

Talking to myself and feeling old,
Sometimes I'd like to quit, nothing ever seems to fit.
Hanging around, nothing to do but frown,
Rainy days and Mondays always get me down.

What I've got they used to call the blues,
Nothing is really wrong, feeling like I don't belong.
Hanging around, some kind of lonely clown,
Rainy days and Mondays always get me down.
Funny, but it seems I always wind up here with you,
Nice to know somebody loves me.
Funny, but it seems that it's the only thing to do,
Run and find the one who loves me.

What I feel has come and gone before,
No need to talk it out, we know what it's all about.
Hanging around, nothing to do but frown,
Rainy days and Mondays always get me down.
Funny, but it seems that it's the only thing to do,
Run and find the one who loves me.

What I feel has come and gone before,
No need to talk it out, we know what it's all about.
Hanging around, nothing to do but frown,
Rainy days and Mondays always get me down.
Hanging around, nothing to do but frown,
Rainy days and Mondays always get me down.

19
REASON TO BELIEVE

If I listened enough to you,
I'd find a way to believe that it's all true,
Knowing that you lied straight-faced, while I cried,
And still I look to find a reason to believe.
Someone like you makes it hard to live without
    somebody else,
Someone like you makes it easy to give, never thinking
    of myself.

If you took the time to change my mind,
I'd find a way to leave the past behind,
Knowing that you lied straight-faced, while I cried,
And still I look to find a reason to believe.
Someone like you makes it hard to live without
    somebody else,
Someone like you makes it easy to give, never thinking
    of myself.

20
SING

Sing, sing a song,
Sing out loud, sing out strong.
Sing of good things, not bad,
Sing of happy, not sad.
Sing, sing a song,
Make it simple to last your whole life long.
Don't worry that it's not good enough for anyone else
    to hear,
Just sing, sing a song.

La la la la la la la la la
La la la la la la la la la.

Sing, sing a song,
Let the world sing along.
Sing of love there could be,
Sing for you, and for me.
Sing, sing a song,
Make it simple to last your whole life long.
Don't worry that it's not good enough for anyone else
    to hear,
Just sing, sing a song.
Just sing, sing a song,
Just sing, sing a song.

La la la la la la la la la la la la
La la la la la la la la la la la la
La la la la la la la la la la la la.

21
MR GUDER

Mister Guder, say Mister Guder,
May I have a moment with you?
For there is something I've got to say,
And please don't let it scare you away.

Mister Guder, say Mister Guder,
I have seen you go through a day,
You're everything a robot lives for.
Walk in at night, and roll out the door at five.

You reflect the company image,
You maintain their rules to live by,
Shine your shoes, let's keep a neat haircut,
Now that you're wearing a coat and tie.

Mister Guder, say Mister Guder,
Some day soon you may realize,
You've blown your life just playing the game,
Where no one wins, but everyone stays the same.

You reflect the company image,
You maintain their rules to live by,
Shine your shoes, let's keep a neat haircut,
Now that you're wearing a coat and tie.

Mister Guder, say Mister Guder,
Some day soon you may realise,
You've blown your life just playing the game,
Where no one wins, but everyone stays the same.

Please play your game,
Stay the same.

22
SOLITAIRE

There was a man, a lonely man,
Who lost his love through his indifference.
A heart that cared, that went unshared,
Until it died within his silence.

And solitaire's the only game in town,
And every road that takes him takes him down,
And by himself, it's easy to pretend he'll never love
    again.
And keeping to himself, he plays the game,
Without her love it always ends the same,
While life goes on around him everywhere,
He's playing solitaire.

A little hope goes up in smoke,
Just how it goes, goes without saying.
There was a man, a lonely man,
Who could command the hand he's playing.

And solitaire's the only game in town,
And every road that takes him takes him down,
And by himself, it's easy to pretend he'll never love
    again.
And keeping to himself, he plays the game,
Without her love it always ends the same,
While life goes on around him everywhere,
He's playing solitaire.

And solitaire's the only game in town,
And every road that takes him takes him down,
While life goes on around him everywhere,
He's playing solitaire.

23
SWEET SWEET SMILE

You're always in my heart,
From early in the mornin' till it's dark,
I gotta see your sweet, sweet smile every day.
When I wake up in the mornin', and I see you there,
I always whisper a little prayer,
I gotta see your sweet, sweet smile every day.

I gotta know that you love me,
And that you want me,
And that you'll always be there,
I've gotta know that you care,
And I gotta feel your arms around me,
And that you need me,
That you'll always be there,
I've got to know that you care.

If my times are bringing me down,
You're the only one that I want around,
I gotta see your sweet, sweet smile every day.
And if I'm all strung out,
You're the only one who can straighten me out,
I gotta see your sweet, sweet smile every day.

I gotta know that you love me,
And that you want me,
And that you'll always be there,
I've gotta know that you care,
And I gotta feel your arms around me,
And that you need me,
That you'll always be there,
I've got to know that you care.

And if I'm all strung out,
You're the only one who can straighten me out,
I gotta see your sweet, sweet smile every day.

I gotta know that you love me,
And that you want me,
And that you'll always be there,
I've gotta know that you care,
And I gotta feel your arms around me,
And that you need me,
That you'll always be there,
I've got to know that you care.

You're always in my heart,
From early in the mornin' till it's dark,
I gotta see your sweet, sweet smile every day.
I gotta see your sweet, sweet smile every day.
I gotta see your sweet, sweet smile every day.

24
SUPERSTAR

Long ago, and oh, so far away,
I fell in love with you, before the second show.
Your guitar, it sounds so sweet and clear,
But you're not really here, it's just the radio.
Don't you remember you told me you loved me baby?
You said you'd be coming back this way again, baby.
Baby, baby, baby, baby, oh baby,
I love you, I really do.

Loneliness is such a sad affair,
And I can hardly wait to be with you again.
What to say to make you come again,
Come back to me again, and play your sad guitar.
Don't you remember you told me you loved me baby?
You said you'd be coming back this way again, baby.
Baby, baby, baby, baby, oh baby,
I love you, I really do.

Don't you remember you told me you loved me baby?
You said you'd be coming back this way again, baby.
Baby, baby, baby, baby, oh baby,
I love you, I really do.

25
THERE'S A KIND
OF HUSH

There's a kind of hush all over the world tonight,
All over the world, you can hear the sound of lovers
 in love.
You know what I mean?
Just the two of us, and nobody else in sight,
There's nobody else,
And I'm feeling good just holding you tight.

So, listen very carefully,
Get closer now, and you will see what I mean,
It isn't a dream.
The only sound that you will hear,
Is when I whisper in your ear, 'I love you,'
Forever and ever.

There's a kind of hush all over the world tonight,
All over the world, people just like us are falling
 in love.
So, listen very carefully,
Get closer now, and you will see what I mean,
It isn't a dream.
The only sound that you will hear,
Is when I whisper in your ear, 'I love you,'
Forever and ever.

There's a kind of hush all over the world tonight,
All over the world , you can hear the sound of lovers
 in love.

26
(THEY LONG TO BE)
CLOSE TO YOU

Why do birds suddenly appear
Every time you are near?
Just like me, they long to be
Close to you.

Why do stars fall down from the sky,
Every time you walk by?
Just like me, they long to be
Close to you.

On the day that you were born, the angels got
 together,
And decided to create a dream come true,
So they sprinkled moondust in your hair of gold,
And starlight in your eyes of blue.

That is why all the girls in town
Follow you around.
Just like me, they long to be
Close to you.

On the day that you were born, the angels got
 together,
And decided to create a dream come true,
So they sprinkled moondust in your hair of gold,
And starlight in your eyes of blue.

That is why all the girls in town,
Follow you all around.
Just like me, they long to be
Close to you.
Just like me, they long to be
Close to you.

Why? Close to you.

27
THIS MASQUERADE

Are we really happy with this lonely game we play?
Looking for the right words to say,
Searching, but not finding, understanding anyway,
We're lost in this masquerade.

Both afraid to say we're just too far away
From being close together from the start,
We tried to talk it over, but the words got in the way,
We're lost inside this lonely game we play.
Thoughts of leaving disappear each time I see your
  eyes,
And no matter how hard I try
To understand the reason why we carry on this way,
We're lost in this masquerade.

We tried to talk it over, but the words got in the way,
We're lost inside this lonely game we play.
Thoughts of leaving disappear each time I see your
  eyes,
And no matter how hard I try
To understand the reason why we carry on this way,
We're lost in this masquerade.

We're lost in this masquerade,
And we're lost in this masquerade.

28
TICKET TO RIDE

I think I'm gonna be sad, I think it's today, yeah,
The boy that's driving me mad is going away.
He's got a ticket to ride, he's got a ticket to ride,
He's got a ticket to ride, and he don't care.

He said that living with me was bringing him down,
  yeah,
He would never be free when I was around.
He's got a ticket to ride, he's got a ticket to ride,
He's got a ticket to ride, and he don't care.

Don't know why he's riding so high,
He ought to do right, he ought to do right by me,
Before he gets to saying goodbye,
He ought to do right, he ought to do right by me.

I think I'm gonna be sad, I think it's today, yeah,
The boy that's driving me mad is going away.
Oh, he's got a ticket to ride, he's got a ticket to ride,
He's got a ticket to ride, and he don't care, care.
Think I'm gonna be sad,
Think I'm gonna be sad.

29
TOP OF THE WORLD

Such a feelin's comin' over me,
There is wonder in most everything I see,
Not a cloud in the sky, got the sun in my eyes,
And I won't be surprised if it's a dream.
Everything I want the world to be
Is now coming true, especially for me,
And the reason is clear, it's because you are here,
You're the nearest thing to heaven that I've seen.

I'm on top of the world lookin' down on creation,
And the only explanation I can find,
Is the love that I've found ever since you've been
    around,
Your love's put me at the top of the world.

Something in the wind has learned my name,
And it's tellin' me that things are not the same.
In the leaves on the trees, and the touch of the breeze,
There's a pleasin' sense of happiness for me.
There is only one wish on my mind,
When this day is through, I hope that I will find
That tomorrow will be just the same for you and me,
All I need will be mine, if you are here.

I'm the on top of the world lookin' down on creation,
And the only explanation I can find,
Is the love that I've found ever since you've been
    around,
Your love's put me at the top of the world.

I'm on top of the world lookin' down on creation,
And the only explanation I can find,
Is the love that I've found ever since you've been
    around,
Your love's put me at the top of the world.

30
WALK ON BY

If you see me walking down the street,
And I start to cry each time we meet,
Walk on by, walk on by,
Make believe that you don't see the tears,
Just let me grieve in private,
'cause each time I see you, I break down and cry.
Walk on by, walk on by, walk on by.

I just can't get over losing you,
And so if I seem broken and blue,
Walk on by, walk on by,
Foolish pride, that's all that I have left,
So let me hide the tears, and the sadness you gave me,
When you said goodbye.
Walk on by, walk on by, walk on by.

31
WE'VE ONLY JUST BEGUN

We've only just begun to live,
White lace and promises,
A kiss for luck, and we're on our way.
We've only just begun.

Before the rising sun, we fly,
So many roads to choose,
We start out walking, and learn to run,
And yes, we've just begun,
Sharing horizons that are new to us,
Watching the signs along the way,
Thinking it over, just the two of us,
Working together day to day, together.

And when the evening comes, we smile,
So much of life ahead,
We'll find a place where there's room to grow,
And yes, we've just begun,
Sharing horizons that are new to us,
Watching the signs along the way,
Thinking it over, just the two of us,
Working together day to day, together, together.

And when the evening comes, we smile,
So much of life ahead,
We'll find a place where there's room to grow,
And yes, we've just begun.

32
YESTERDAY ONCE MORE

When I was young, I'd listen to the radio,
Waitin' for my fav'rite songs,
When they played I'd sing along, it made me smile.
Those were such happy times,
And not so long ago,
How I wondered where they'd gone,
But they're back again,
Just like a long lost friend, all the songs I love so well.

Every sha-la-la-la, every wo woo still shines,
Every shing-a-ling-a-ling that they're startin' to sing,
    so fine.
When they get to the part where he's breaking her
    heart,
It can really make me cry, just like before,
It's yesterday once more,
Shoobie do lang lang.

Lookin' back on how it was in years gone by,
And the good times that I had,
Makes today seem rather sad,
So much has changed.
It was songs of love that I would sing to them,
And I'd memorise each word,
Those old melodies still sound so good to me,
As they melt the years away.

Every sha-la-la-la, every wo woo still shines,
Every shing-a-ling-a-ling that they're startin' to sing,
    so fine.
All my best memories come back clearly to me,
Some can even make me cry, just like before,
It's yesterday once more.

Every sha-la-la-la, every wo woo still shines,
Every shing-a-ling-a-ling that they're startin' to sing,
    so fine.

THE MUSIC

1

A SONG FOR YOU

WORDS & MUSIC BY LEON RUSSELL

1. I've been so ma-ny pla - ces in my life and time,
2. I know your i-mage of me is what I hope to be,
(3.) love you in a place where there's no space or time, I'll
4. (Instrumental)
5. (Instrumental)

I've sung a lot of songs, I've made some bad rhyme, I've
I've treat-ed you un-kind - ly, but dar - ling, can't you see? There's
love you, for in my life you are a friend of mine, and

act-ed out my love in sta-ges, with ten thou - sand peo - ple watch - ing,
no-one more im-port-ant to me, dar-ling, can't you please see through me?
when my life is o - ver, re - mem-ber when we were to-ge - ther,

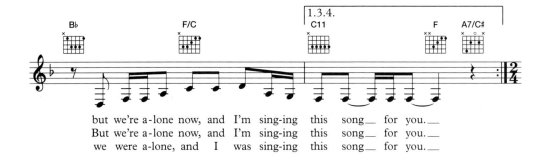

but we're a-lone now, and I'm sing-ing this song for you.
But we're a-lone now, and I'm sing-ing this song for you.
we were a-lone, and I was sing-ing this song for you.

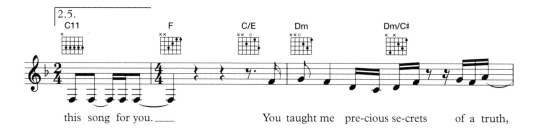

this song for you.___ You taught me pre-cious se-crets of a truth,

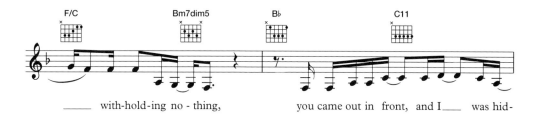

___ with-hold-ing no - thing, you came out in front, and I___ was hid-

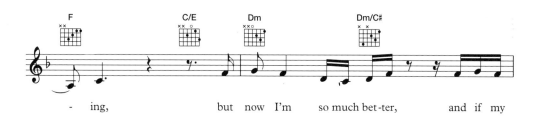

- ing, but now I'm so much bet-ter, and if my

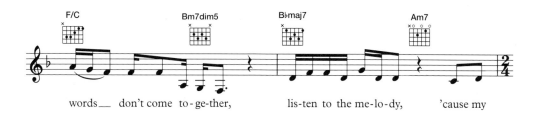

words__ don't come to-ge-ther, lis-ten to the me-lo-dy, 'cause my

love is in there hid - ing,___ ooh._____ 3. I'll

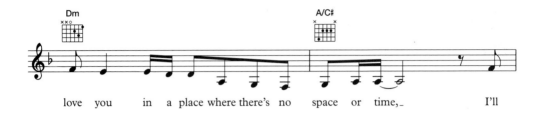

love you in a place where there's no space or time,_ I'll

love you, for in my life___ you are a friend of mine, and

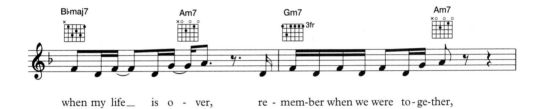

when my life_ is o - ver, re - mem-ber when we were to-ge-ther,

we were a-lone, and I was sing-ing this song__ for you,

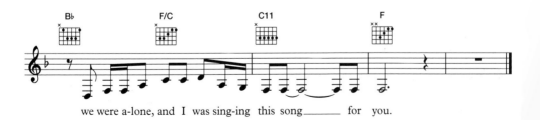

we were a-lone, and I was sing-ing this song_____ for you.

ANOTHER SONG

WORDS BY JOHN BETTIS. MUSIC BY RICHARD CARPENTER

(Instrumental) The moon that rose, now de-scend-ed, and the love one shared now had end-ed, and soon the day_ would come. (Instrumental)

And_ when the day_ had_ come, the light that fell at dawn was cold, the warmth of you had gone._

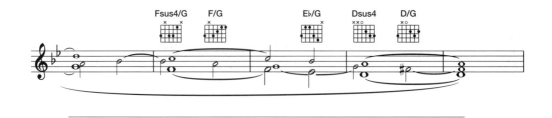

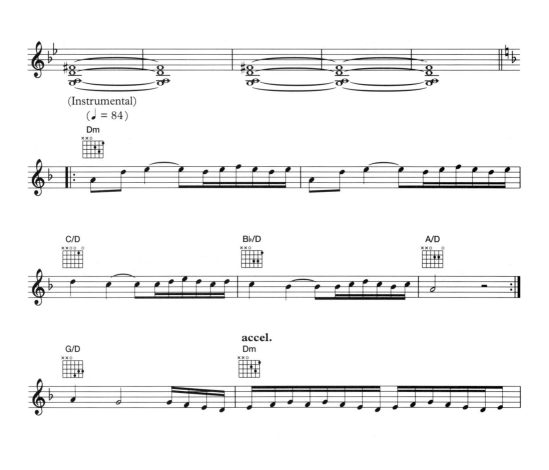

(Instrumental)
($\quad$ = 84)

accel.

($\quad$ = 112)

(Instrumental *sim.*)

3
CAN'T SMILE WITHOUT YOU

WORDS & MUSIC BY CHRIS ARNOLD, DAVID MARTIN & GEOFF MORROW

(Instrumental)

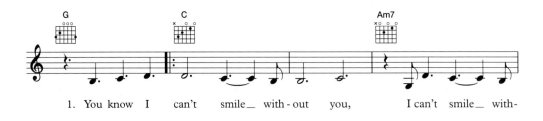

1. You know I can't smile_ with-out you, I can't smile_ with-

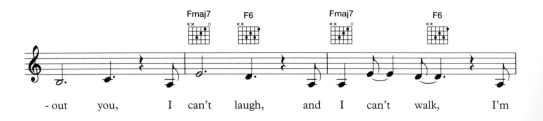

- out you, I can't laugh, and I can't walk, I'm

(Instrumental)

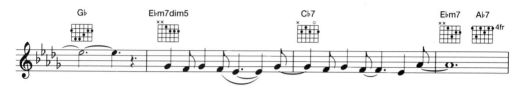

In - to the new,___ leav - ing the old_ be - hind___

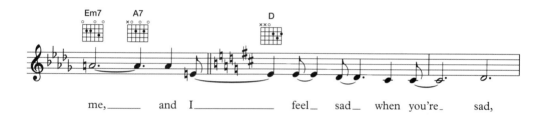

me,___ and I___ feel_ sad_ when you're_ sad,

I feel glad__ when you're glad, and you must know what I'm

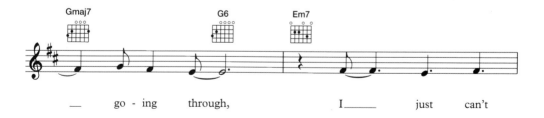

__ go - ing through, I___ just can't

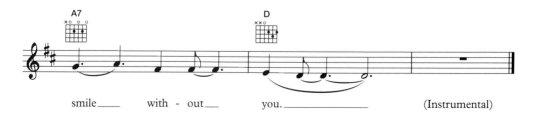

smile___ with - out__ you.___ (Instrumental)

4

CRYSTAL LULLABY

WORDS BY JOHN BETTIS. MUSIC BY RICHARD CARPENTER

(Instrumental)

Lis - ten to the song he sings. Can't you see his mu - sic

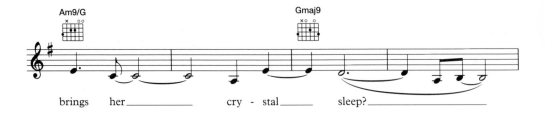

brings her_____ cry - stal_____ sleep?_____

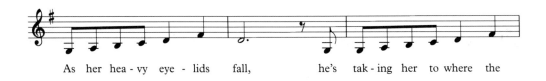

As her hea - vy eye - lids fall, he's tak - ing her to where the

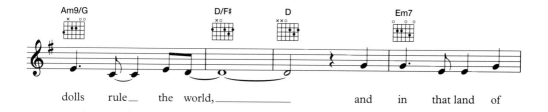

dolls　rule＿　the　world,＿＿＿＿＿　　　and　in　that　land　of

make　be-lieve,　is　where＿　he'll　leave　her　sleep-ing,＿＿

soft - ly　warm　　in　a　cry-stal　lul - la　-　by.＿＿＿＿＿　He's

weav-ing　her　a　pa - per　cas - tle,　　where　danc-ing　clowns　with　tass - les

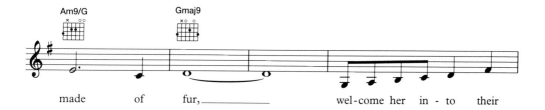

made　　of　fur,＿＿＿＿＿　　wel-come　her　in - to　their

world, that lives in-side the dreams of ev - ery lit - tle girl._____

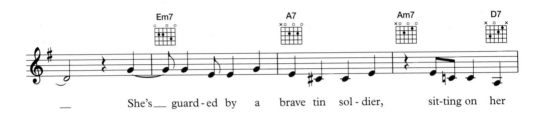

_ She's__ guard-ed by a brave tin sol - dier, sit-ting on her

shoul - der,_____ tak - en there_____ in a cry-stal lul - la -

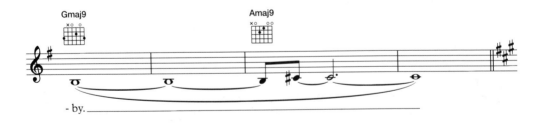

- by. _____

1. Some-times, when I lis - ten to the vel-vet song, that fills the
(*2nd time* Instrumental)

5

DO YOU KNOW THE WAY TO SAN JOSE

WORDS BY HAL DAVID. MUSIC BY BURT BACHARACH

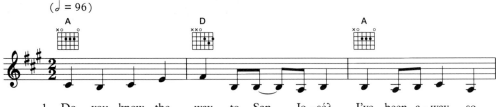

1. Do you know the way to San_ Jo-sé? I've been a-way so
2. You can real-ly breathe in San_ Jo-sé, they've got a lot of

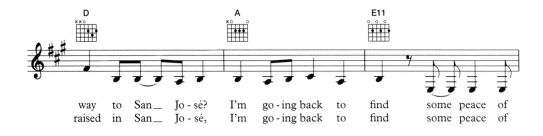

long, I__ may go wrong, and lose__ my way. Do you know the
space, there'll be a place where I__ can stay. I was born and

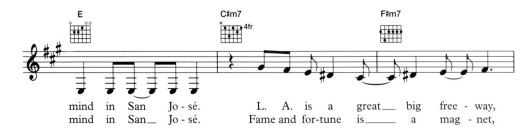

way to San_ Jo-sé? I'm go-ing back to find some peace of
raised in San_ Jo-sé, I'm go-ing back to find some peace of

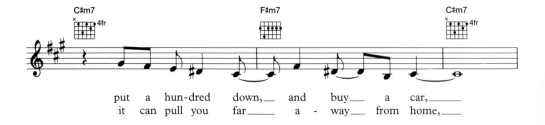

mind in San Jo-sé. L. A. is a great__ big free-way,
mind in San_ Jo-sé. Fame and for-tune is__ a mag-net,

put a hun-dred down,__ and buy__ a car,__
it can pull you far__ a-way__ from home,__

in a week, may-be two, they'll make you a star,___
with a dream in your heart, you're ne - ver a - lone,___

weeks turn in - to years,___ how quick they pass, and all the stars
dreams turn in - to dust,___ and blow a - way, and there you are___

___ that ne-ver were___ are park-ing cars,___ and pump-ing gas.
___ with-out a friend, now pack the car___ and ride_ a - way.

I've got lots of friends in San_ Jo - sé (Instrumental)

Can't wait to get back to San___ Jo - sé. (Instrumental)

Do you know the way to San___ Jo - sé?

repeat ad lib. to fade

(Instrumental)

6

BREAKING UP IS HARD TO DO

WORDS & MUSIC BY NEIL SEDAKA & HOWARD GREENFIELD
© COPYRIGHT 1962 SCREEN GEMS-EMI MUSIC INCORPORATED, USA.
SUB-PUBLISHED BY SCREEN GEMS-EMI MUSIC LIMITED, 127 CHARING CROSS ROAD, LONDON WC2.
ALL RIGHTS RESERVED. INTERNATIONAL COPYRIGHT SECURED.

($\quad$ = 126)

Come - a come - a down do - be do dum down,__ come - a come - a

down do - be do dum down,_ come - a come - a down do - be do dum down,

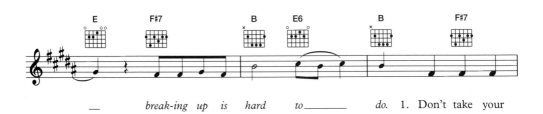

__ break-ing up is hard to_____ do. 1. Don't take your

love_____ a - way from me,__ don't you leave my heart in

mi - se - ry,__ if you go then I'll be blue,__ 'cause

7

DON'T CRY FOR ME ARGENTINA

MUSIC BY ANDREW LLOYD WEBBER. LYRICS BY TIM RICE.

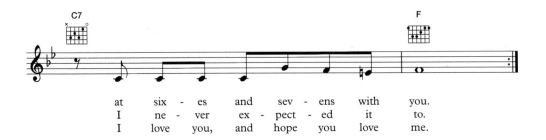

at six - es and sev - ens with you.
I ne - ver ex - pect - ed it to.
I love you, and hope you love me.

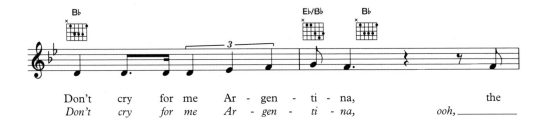

Don't cry for me Ar - gen - ti - na, the
Don't cry for me Ar - gen - ti - na, *ooh, _____*

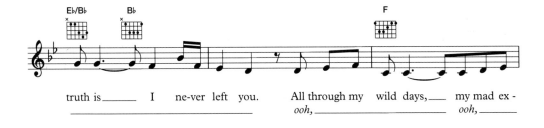

truth is_____ I ne-ver left you. All through my wild days,___ my mad ex -
ooh, _____ *ooh, _____*

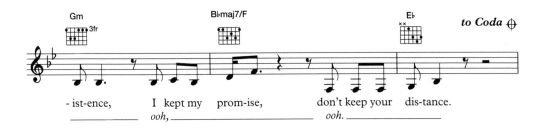

- ist-ence, I kept my prom-ise, don't keep your dis-tance.
_____ ooh, _____ *ooh. _____*

Don't cry for me Ar - gen - ti - na, the

truth is_____ I ne-ver left you. All through my wild days,___ my mad ex -

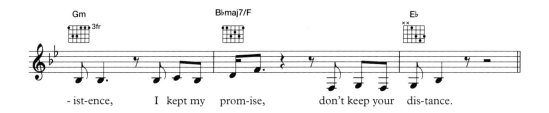

- ist-ence, I kept my prom-ise, don't keep your dis-tance.

Have I said too much? There's no-thing more I can think of to

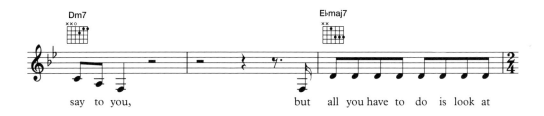

say to you, but all you have to do is look at

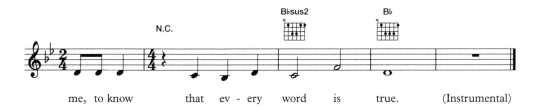

me, to know that ev - ery word is true. (Instrumental)

8

FOR ALL WE KNOW

WORDS BY ROBB WILSON & ARTHUR JAMES. MUSIC BY FRED KARLIN

(Instrumental)

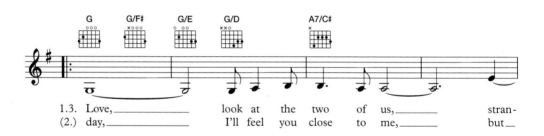

1.3. Love,_____ look at the two of us,_____ stran-
(2.) day,_____ I'll feel you close to me,_____ but__

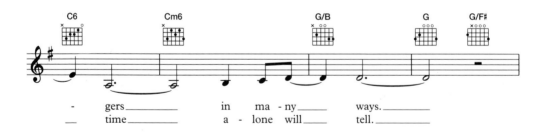

- gers_____ in ma - ny_____ ways._____
__ time_____ a - lone will__ tell._____

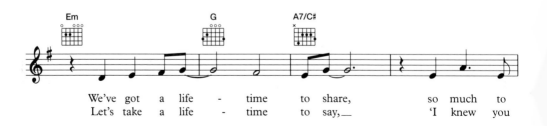

We've got a life - time to share, so much to
Let's take a life - time to say,__ 'I knew you

say,_____ and as we go_____ from___ day to
well,'_____ for on - ly time_____

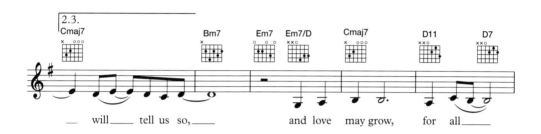

___ will____ tell us so,_____ and love may grow, for all_____

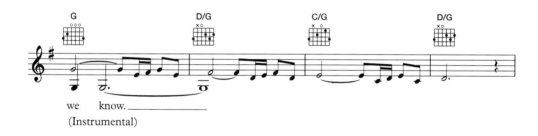

we know._____
(Instrumental)

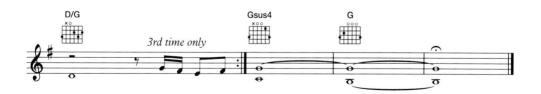

3rd time only

9
GOODBYE TO LOVE

WORDS BY JOHN BETTIS. MUSIC BY RICHARD CARPENTER

1. I'll say good - bye to love, no-one ev - er cared if I__ should
(2.) - bye to love, there are no to - mor - rows for this

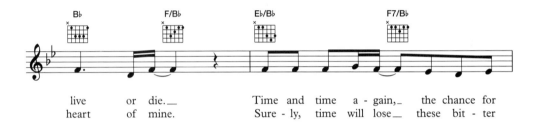

live or die.__ Time and time a - gain,__ the chance for
heart of mine. Sure - ly, time will lose__ these bit - ter

love has passed me by,__ and all I know of love is how to live__ with-out
mem-ories, and I'll find__ that there is some-one to be-lieve in, and__ to live

__ it,__ I just can't seem to find___ it.
__ for,__ some-thing I could live___ for.

So, I've made my mind up, I must live my life a - lone, and
All the years of use - less search have fi - nally reached an end,

though it's not the ea - sy way, I guess I've al - ways known. 2. I'd say good -
lone - li - ness and emp - ty days will

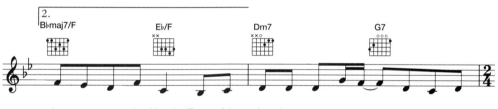

be my on - ly friend. From this day love is for - got - ten, I'll go

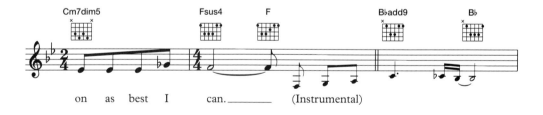

on as best I can._____ (Instrumental)

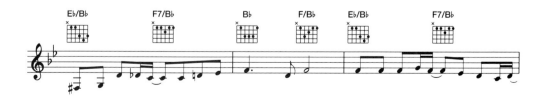

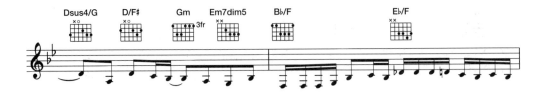

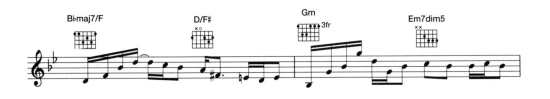

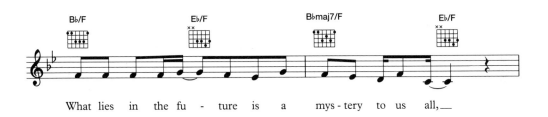

What lies in the fu – ture is a mys - tery to us all, __

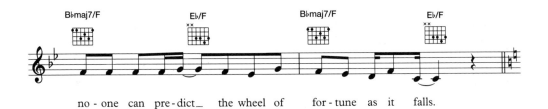

no - one can pre - dict_ the wheel of for - tune as it falls.

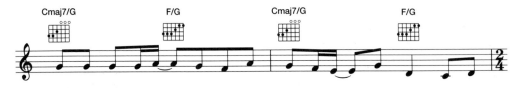

There may come a time when I will see that I've_ been wrong, but for

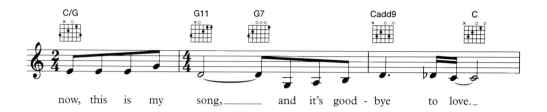

now, this is my song,_____ and it's good - bye to love._

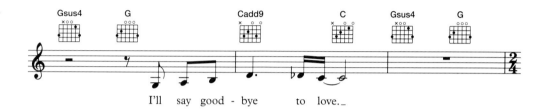

I'll say good - bye to love._

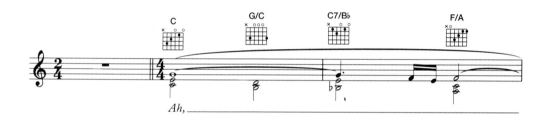

*Ah,*_____

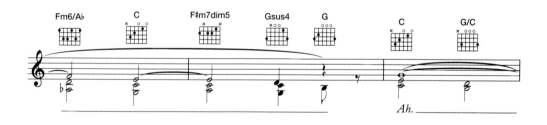

_____ *Ah.*_____

repeat ad lib. to fade

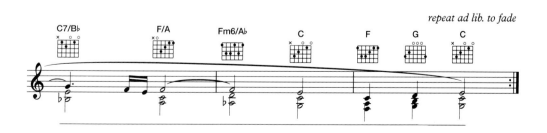

_____

HURTING EACH OTHER

WORDS BY PETER UDELL. MUSIC BY GARY GELD.

1. No - one___ in the world ev - er___ had a love as sweet as___
2. Clo - ser___ than the leaves on a___ weep-in' wil - low, ba - by,___

___ my___ love,___ for no-where in the world
___ we___ are,___ clo - ser dear, are we,

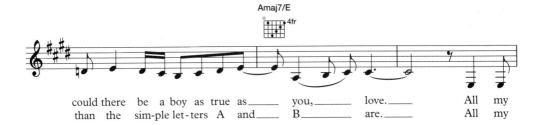

could there be a boy as true as___ you,___ love.___ All my
than the sim-ple let-ters A and___ B___ are.___ All my

love,___ I give glad - ly to you, all your love, you give
life,___ I could love on - ly you, all your life, you could

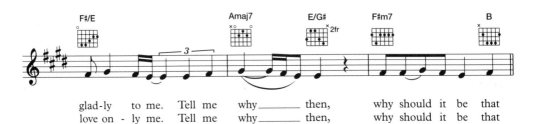

glad - ly to me. Tell me why___ then, why should it be that
love on - ly me. Tell me why___ then, why should it be that

11
I WON'T LAST A DAY WITHOUT YOU

WORDS BY PAUL WILLIAMS. MUSIC BY ROGER NICHOLS

(Instrumental)

1. Day af-ter day,_ I must face a world of stran-gers,_ where I
2. So ma-ny times, when the ci-ty seems to be_ with-out a

don't be-long,_ I'm not that strong.
friend-ly face,_ a lone-ly place.

It's nice to know that there's some-one I_ can turn to,_ who will al-
It's nice to know that you'll be there if_ I need you,_ and you'll al-

- ways care,_ you're al-ways there.
- ways smile, it's all worth-while. When there's

no get-ting o-ver_ that rain-bow,_ when my

touch me with the love_ you're bring - ing,_____

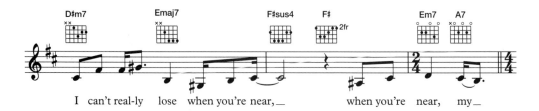

I can't real-ly lose when you're near,_ when you're near, my_

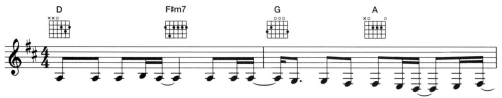

love. 3. If all my friends have for-got - ten half their prom - is - es,_ they're not

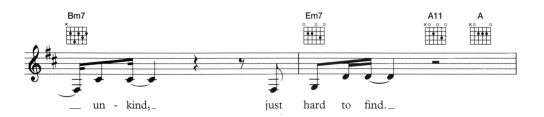

_ un - kind,_ just hard to find._

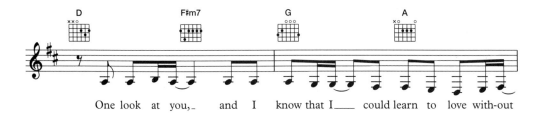

One look at you,_ and I know that I___ could learn to love with-out

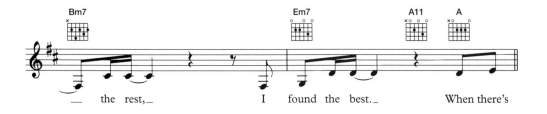

_ the rest,_ I found the best._ When there's

12
I NEED TO BE IN LOVE

WORDS & MUSIC BY RICHARD CARPENTER, JOHN BETTIS & ALBERT HAMMOND
© COPYRIGHT 1976 ALMO MUSIC CORPORATION, HAMMER AND NAILS MUSIC AND LANDERS-ROBERTS MUSIC, USA.
RONDOR MUSIC (LONDON) LIMITED, 10A PARSONS GREEN, LONDON SW6 (66 2/3%)/
EMPIRE MUSIC LIMITED, 27 QUEENSDALE PLACE, LONDON W11 (33 1/3%).

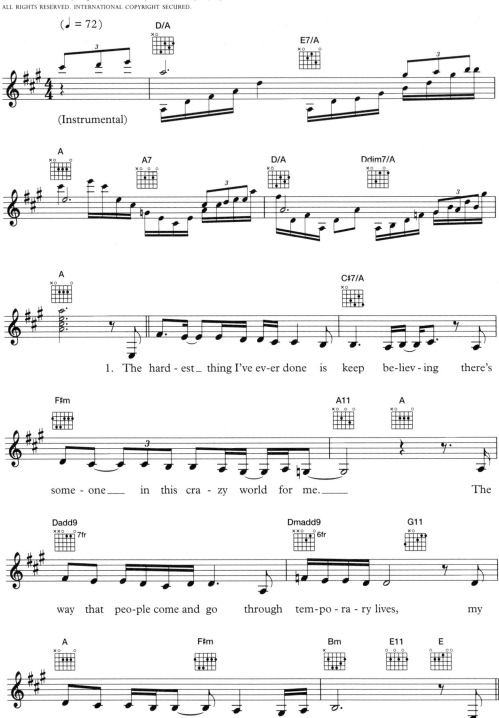

(Instrumental)

1. The hard - est_ thing I've ev-er done is keep be-liev-ing there's

some - one____ in this cra - zy world for me.____ The

way that peo-ple come and go through tem-po-ra-ry lives, my

chance could come and I_____ might ne - ver know. 2. I

13

I'LL NEVER FALL IN LOVE AGAIN

WORDS BY HAL DAVID. MUSIC BY BURT BACHARACH

(♩ = 138)

Capo 3

(Instrumental)

Here to re - mind_ you, here to re - mind_ you, here to re - mind_ you,

here to re - mind____ you,____

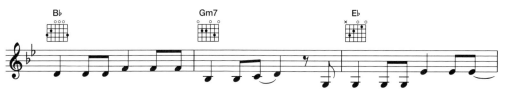

1. What do you get when you fall in love? A guy with a pin to burst

_ your bub - ble, that's what you get for all____ your trou-ble, I'll____

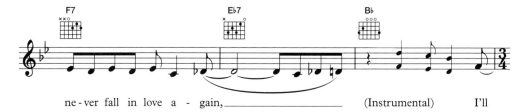

ne - ver fall in love a - gain,____ (Instrumental) I'll

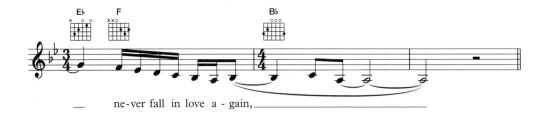

Don't tell me what it's all a-bout, 'cause I've been there, and I'm

glad_ I'm out,_____ out of those chains, those chains that bind_____ you.

That is why I'm here to re - mind_____ you, here to re - mind you,

here to re - mind you, here to re - mind you, here to re - mind you._____

(Instrumental)

D.𝄋 al Coda   ⊕ ***CODA***

(Instrumental)

14

IT'S GOING TO TAKE SOME TIME

WORDS & MUSIC BY CAROLE KING & TONI STERN

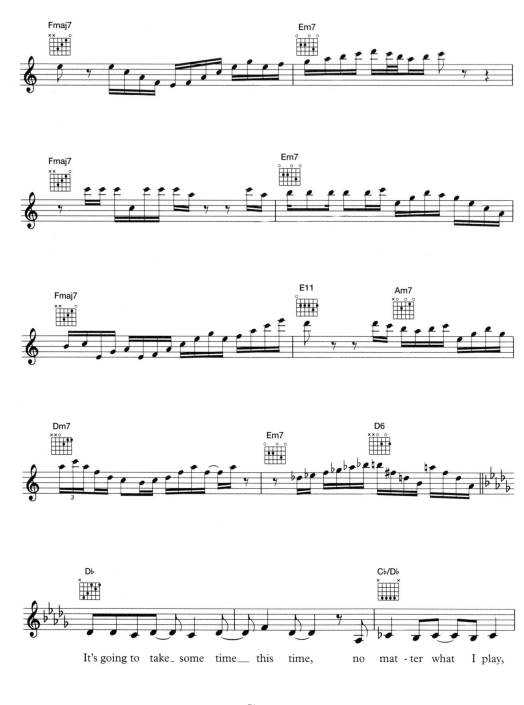

It's going to take_ some time_ this time, no mat-ter what I play,

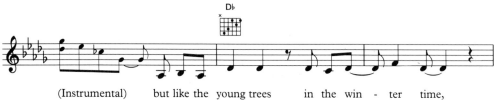

(Instrumental) but like the young trees in the win - ter time,

15
JAMBALAYA (ON THE BAYOU)

WORDS & MUSIC BY HANK WILLIAMS

(♩ = 100)

(Instrumental)

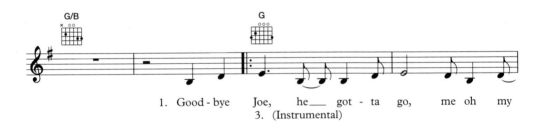

1. Good - bye Joe, he__ got - ta go, me oh my
3. (Instrumental)

__ oh, he got - ta go pole the pi - rogue down the bay - ou.

His Y - vonne, the sweet-est one,__ me oh my__ oh,

son of a gun, __ we'll have __ big fun on the bay - ou.

2. Thi - bo - deaux, Foun - tain - eaux, __ the place is buzz - in',
4. Set - tle down, far from town, __ get him a pi - rogue,

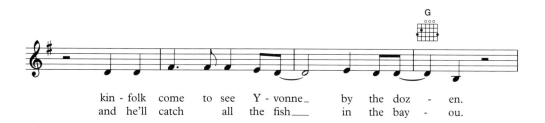

kin - folk come to see Y - vonne __ by the doz - en.
and he'll catch all the fish __ in the bay - ou.

Dressed in style, they go hog - wild, me oh my __ oh,
Swap his mon to buy Y - vonne what she need - o,

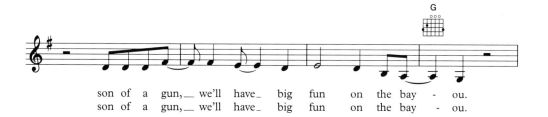

son of a gun, __ we'll have __ big fun on the bay - ou.
son of a gun, __ we'll have __ big fun on the bay - ou.

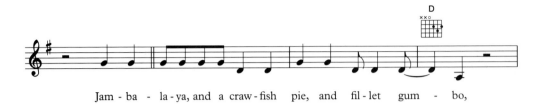

Jam - ba - la - ya, and a craw - fish pie, and fil - let gum - bo,

for to - night_ I'm gon - na see___ my ma cher a - mi - o,

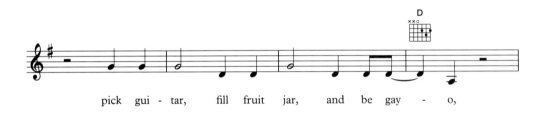

pick gui - tar, fill fruit jar, and be gay - o,

to Coda ⊕

son of a gun,___ we'll have big fun on the bay - ou.

⊕ *CODA*

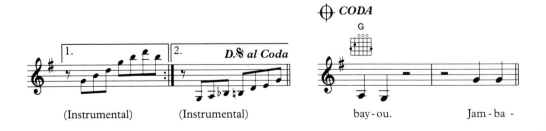

1.

(Instrumental)

2. *D.S al Coda*

(Instrumental)

bay - ou.

Jam - ba -

-la - ya, and a craw - fish pie, and fil - let gum - bo,

for to - night__ I'm gon - na see___ my ma cher a - mi - o,

pick gui - tar, fill fruit jar, and be gay - o,

son of a gun,__ we'll have big fun on the bay - ou.

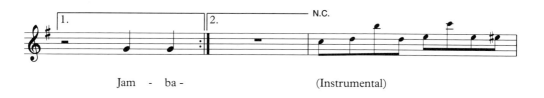

Jam - ba - (Instrumental)

16
LET ME BE THE ONE

WORDS BY PAUL WILLIAMS. MUSIC BY ROGER NICHOLS
© COPYRIGHT 1970 BY ALMO MUSIC CORPORATION, USA.
RIGHTS FOR THE UNITED KINGDOM AND EIRE CONTROLLED BY RONDOR MUSIC (LONDON) LIMITED, 10A PARSON'S GREEN, LONDON SW6.
ALL RIGHTS RESERVED. INTERNATIONAL COPYRIGHT SECURED.

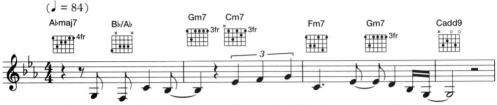

1. Some sleep-less night, ___ if you should find your-self a-lone, ___
2. To set things right, ___ when this old world's turned up-side down,

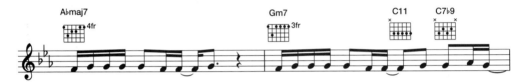

let me be the one you run ___ to, let me be the one you come to when you need
let me be the one you run ___ to, let me be the one you come to when you need

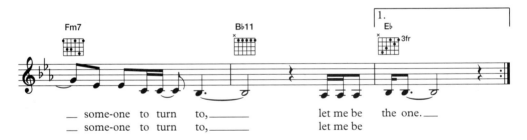

___ some-one to turn to, _____ let me be the one. ___
___ some-one to turn to, _____ let me be

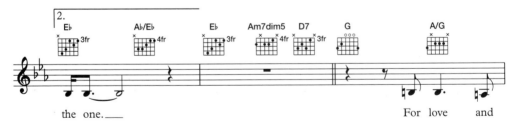

the one. ___ For love and

un-der-stand-ing, ___ to find a qui-et place,

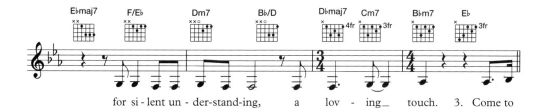

for si-lent un-der-stand-ing,   a   lov - ing_ touch.   3. Come to

me when things go   wrong,   and there's no   love   to_ light the way,_

let me be the one you run _ to,   let me be the one you come to when you need

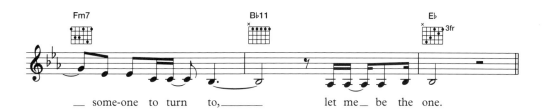

_ some-one to turn   to,_____   let me_ be the one.

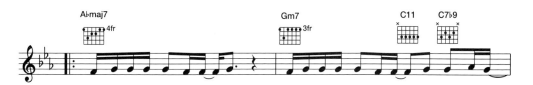

Let me be the one you run to,   let me be the one you come to when you need

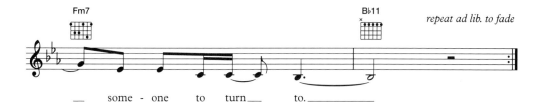

_   some - one   to   turn_   to. _____

17

PLEASE MR POSTMAN

WORDS & MUSIC BY B. HOLLAND & F.C. GORMAN
© COPYRIGHT 1962 JOBETE MUSIC COMPANY, USA.
DOMINION MUSIC LIMITED, 127 CHARING CROSS ROAD, LONDON WC2.

Stop! Whoah yes, wait a min-ute Mis-ter Post-man, wait! Wait_____

_____ Mis-ter Post-man. Please Mis-ter Post-man, look and see,_

if there's a let-ter in your bag for me._ Why's it tak-ing

such a long time, for me to hear from that boy of mine?

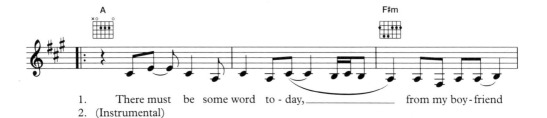

1. There must be some word to-day,_____ from my boy-friend
2. (Instrumental)

so far a - way.＿　　　　Please Mis-ter Post-man,　　look and　see,＿

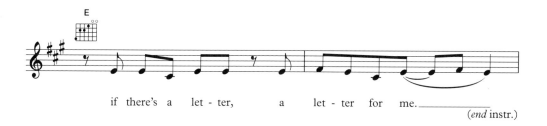

if there's a　let - ter,　　a　let - ter　for　me.＿＿＿＿＿＿＿＿
(end instr.)

I've been stand-ing here　wait-ing, Mis-ter Post-man,　　　so＿＿＿＿＿
So ma-ny days　　you passed　me by,＿＿＿＿　　see the tears stand-ing

pa-tient - ly,＿＿＿＿＿　　for just a card,　　　or just a let-ter,
in my　eyes.＿＿＿＿　You did-n't stop　to make me feel　bet-ter,

say - ing he's re - turn - ing　home＿ to me.＿＿＿＿
but ev - en me,＿　I　got her a　let - ter, *Mis - ter*

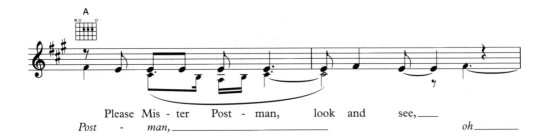

Please Mis - ter Post - man, look and see,____ oh_____

Post - man, _____

if there's a let - ter in your bag for me.____

— yeah, _____ *please, —* *please*

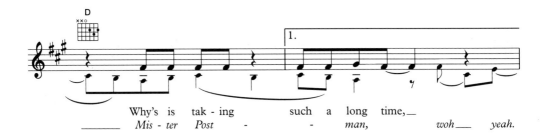

1.

Why's is tak - ing such a long time,____ woh___ yeah.

Mis - ter Post - - man,

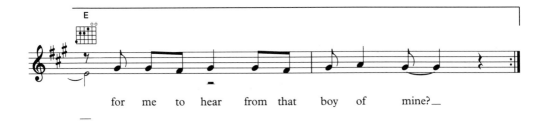

for me to hear from that boy of mine?__

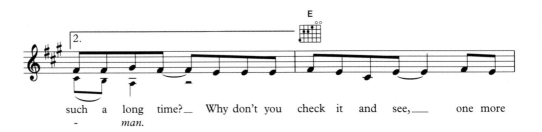

2.

such a long time?__ Why don't you check it and see,____ one more

- man.

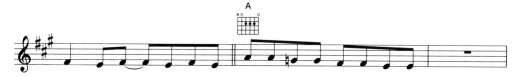

time for me?__ You got to wait a min-ute, wait a min-ute,

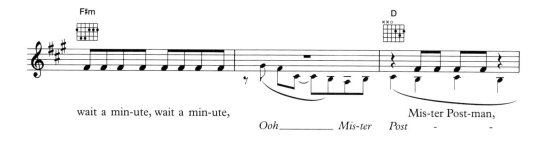

wait a min-ute, wait a min-ute,

Ooh_____ Mis-ter Post - -

Mis-ter Post-man,

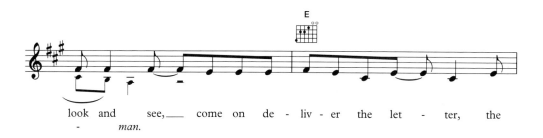

look and see,__ come on de - liv - er the let - ter, the

- man.

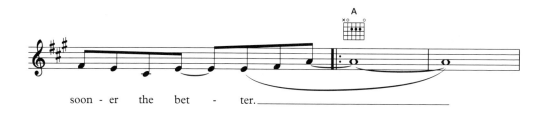

soon - er the bet - ter._____

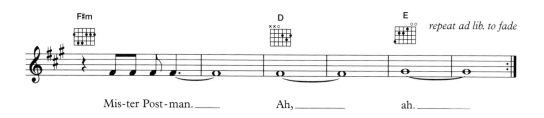

repeat ad lib. to fade

Mis-ter Post-man.____ Ah,_____ ah._____

18
RAINY DAYS AND MONDAYS

WORDS BY PAUL WILLIAMS. MUSIC BY ROGER NICHOLS.

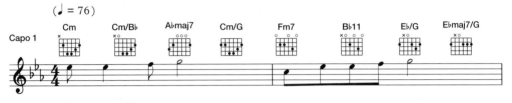

(Instrumental)

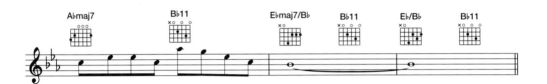

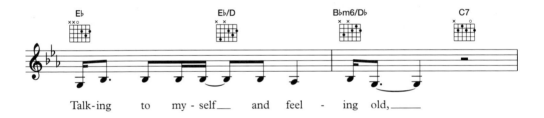

Talk-ing to my-self___ and feel - ing old,_____

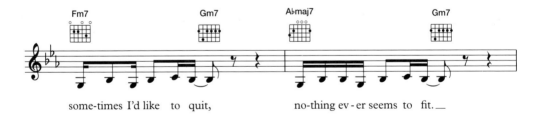

some-times I'd like to quit, no-thing ev - er seems to fit. __

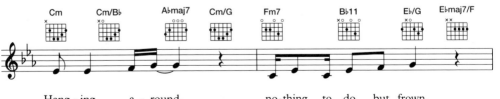

Hang - ing a - round, no-thing to do but frown,

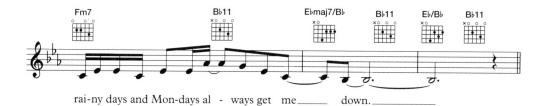

rai-ny days and Mon-days al - ways get me_____ down._____

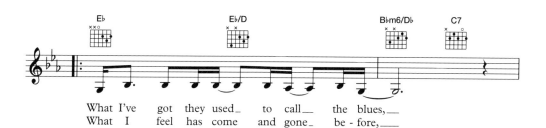

What I've got they used_ to call__ the blues,___
What I feel has come and gone_ be - fore,____

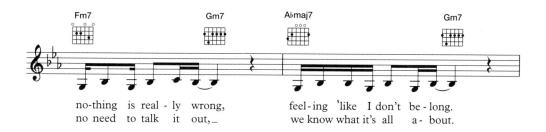

no-thing is real - ly wrong, feel-ing 'like I don't be - long.
no need to talk it out,_ we know what it's all a - bout.

Hang - ing a - round, some kind of lone - ly clown,
Hang - ing a - round, no - thing to do but frown,

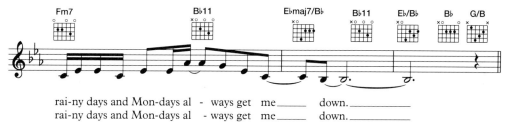

rai-ny days and Mon-days al - ways get me_____ down._____
rai-ny days and Mon-days al - ways get me_____ down._____

Fun-ny, but it seems I al-ways wind up here with you,—
(2nd time Instrumental)

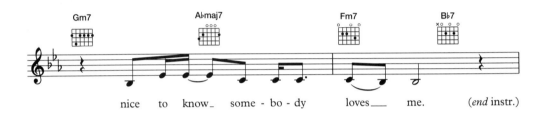

nice to know— some-bo-dy loves— me. (end instr.)

Fun-ny, but it seems that it's— the on - ly thing to do,—

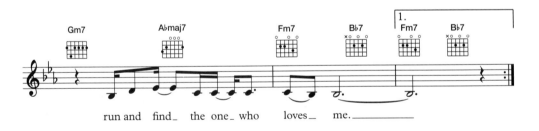

run and find— the one— who loves— me. _____

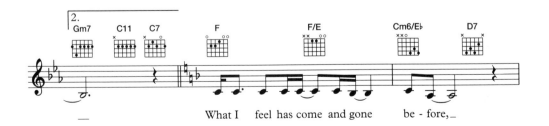

__ What I feel has come and gone be - fore,—

19
REASON TO BELIEVE

WORDS & MUSIC BY TIM HARDIN

(♩ = 84)

(Instrumental)

1. If I lis-tened long e-nough to___ you, I'd find a way
2. If you took the time to change my___ mind, I'd find a way

_____ to be-lieve that it's all___ true,_ know-ing___ that you lied
_____ to leave the past be-hind, know-ing___ that you lied

— straight-faced, while I cried,___ and still I
— straight-faced, while I cried,___ and still I

look to find a rea-son to be-lieve.___
look to find a rea-son to be-lieve.___ Some-one like

you makes it hard_ to live with-out___ some-bo-dy else,

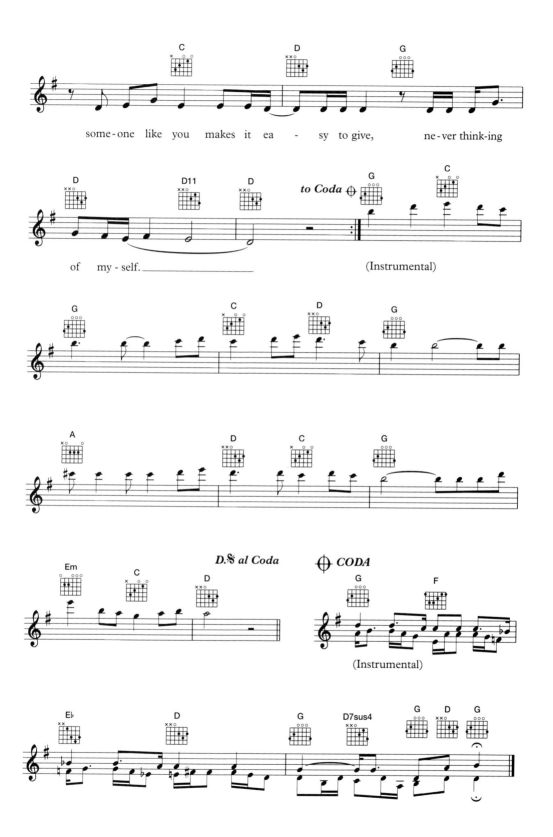

some-one like you makes it ea - sy to give, ne - ver think-ing

to Coda

of my - self. _____ (Instrumental)

D.%. al Coda **CODA**

(Instrumental)

SING

WORDS & MUSIC BY JOE RAPOSO

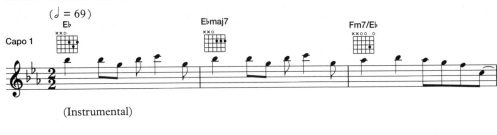

(Instrumental)

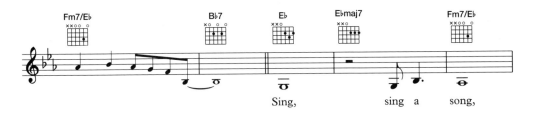

Sing,   sing a song,

sing out   loud,   sing out_____ strong._____

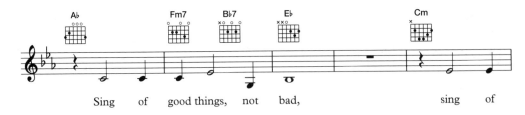

Sing   of   good things,   not   bad,   sing   of

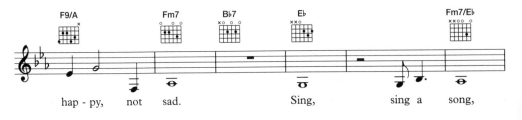

hap - py,   not   sad.   Sing,   sing a   song,

make it sim-ple to last your whole life____ long.____ Don't

wor-ry that it's not good e-nough for a-ny-one else to

hear, just sing, sing a song.____
(Instrumental)

La la la la la la la la la la la la la la la la la.____

Sing, sing a song, let the world

MR GUDER

WORDS BY JOHN BETTIS. MUSIC BY RICHARD CARPENTER

(Instrumental)

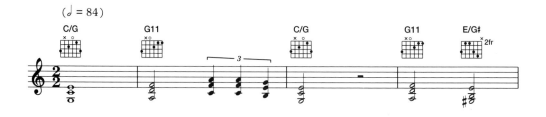

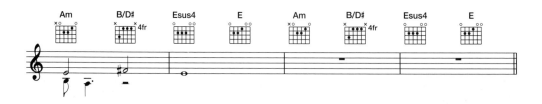

1. Mis - ter Gud-er, say Mis - ter Gud-er, may I___ have a
2. Mis - ter Gud-er, say Mis - ter Gud-er, I have seen you

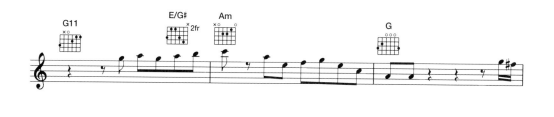

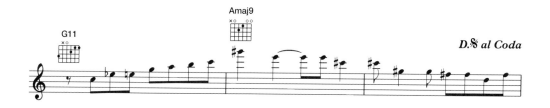

D.% al Coda*

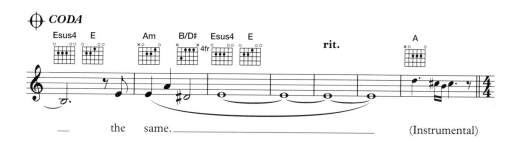

⊕ *CODA*

rit.

___ the   same._____ (Instrumental)

(♩ = 92)

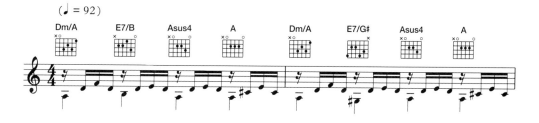

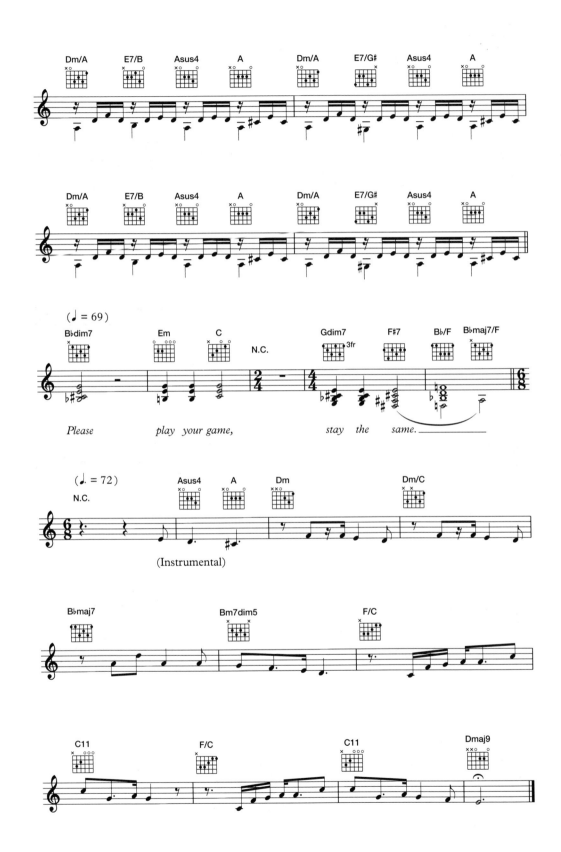

22
SOLITAIRE

WORDS & MUSIC BY PHILIP CODY & NEIL SEDAKA
© COPYRIGHT 1972 & 1975 NEIL SEDAKA MUSIC INCORPORATED, USA.
REPRINTED BY PERMISSION OF WARNER CHAPPELL MUSIC LIMITED, 129 PARK STREET, LONDON W1.
ALL RIGHTS RESERVED. INTERNATIONAL COPYRIGHT SECURED.

(Instrumental)

1. There was___
2. A lit -

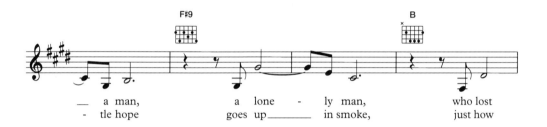

___ a man,   a lone - ly man,   who lost
- tle hope   goes up_____ in smoke,   just how

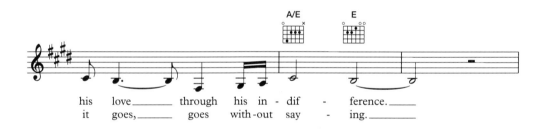

his love_____ through his in - dif - ference.____
it goes,_____ goes with-out say - ing._____

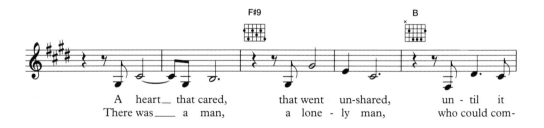

A heart_ that cared,   that went un-shared,   un - til it
There was_____ a man,   a lone - ly man,   who could com-

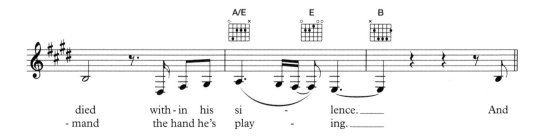

died with - in his si - lence.____   And
- mand the hand he's play - ing._____

so - li-taire's the on - ly game_ in town, and

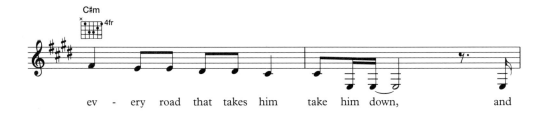

ev - ery road that takes him take him down, and

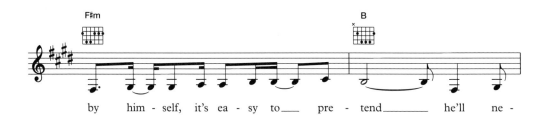

by him - self, it's ea - sy to__ pre - tend__ he'll ne -

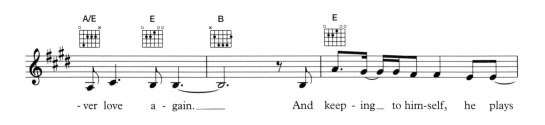

- ver love a - gain.__ And keep - ing_ to him-self, he plays

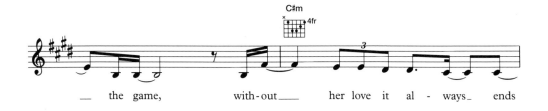

_ the game, with - out__ her love it al - ways_ ends

23
SWEET SWEET SMILE

WORDS & MUSIC BY JUICE NEWTON & OTHA YOUNG
© COPYRIGHT 1977 STERLING MUSIC, USA.
CAMPBELL CONNELLY & COMPANY LIMITED, 8/9 FRITH STREET, LONDON W1.

(Instrumental)

You're al - ways in my heart, from

ear - ly in the morn-in' till it's dark,_ I got - ta see your sweet, sweet

smile ev - ery day. ___   When I wake up in the morn-in', and I

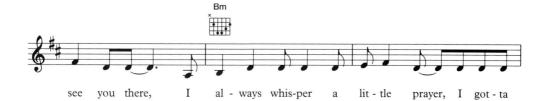

see you there, I al - ways whis-per a lit - tle prayer, I got - ta

see your sweet, sweet smile ev - ery day. ___   I got - ta

know that you love me, ___ and that you want me, ___

and that you'll al - ways be there, ___ I've got - ta know ___

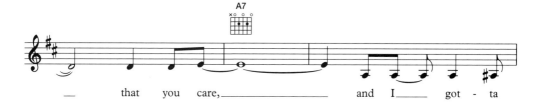

___ that you care, ___ and I ___ got - ta

feel your arms a - round me,___ and that you need me,___

that you'll al - ways be there,___ I've got - ta know_____

___ that you care._____

1. If my times are
2. Instrumental
3. You're al - ways

bring - ing me down,_ you're the on - ly one that I___
in my heart,_ from ear - ly in the morn - in' till__

___ want a - round, I got - ta see your sweet, sweet
___ it's dark,___ I got - ta see your sweet, sweet

1.2.

smile ev - ery day.___ And if___ I'm all_
smile ev - ery day.___

strung out, you're the only one who can

straight-en me out, I got-ta see your sweet, sweet

smile ev-ery day. I got-ta
I got-ta

3.
I got-ta see your sweet, sweet smile ev-ery day.

I got-ta see your sweet, sweet

smile ev-ery day.

24
SUPERSTAR

WORDS & MUSIC BY LEON RUSSELL & BONNIE BRAMLETT
© COPYRIGHT 1970 TEDDY JACK MUSIC, USA.
RONDOR MUSIC (LONDON) LIMITED, 10A PARSONS GREEN, LONDON SW6.

(Instrumental)

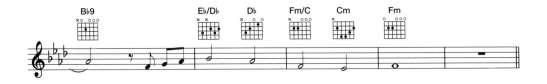

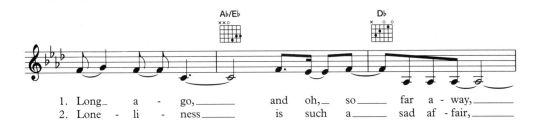

1. Long a - go, and oh, so far a - way,
2. Lone - li - ness is such a sad af - fair,

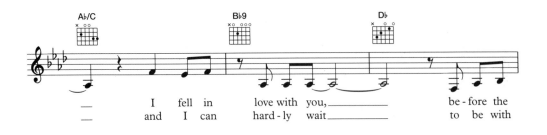

— I fell in love with you, be - fore the
— and I can hard - ly wait to be with

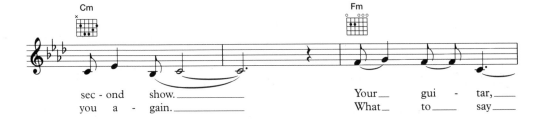

sec - ond show. Your gui - tar,
you a - gain. What to say

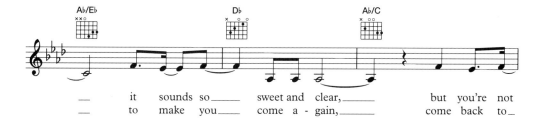

| | it | sounds | so___ | sweet and | clear,___ | | but you're | not |
| | to | make | you___ | come a - | gain,___ | | come | back | to_ |

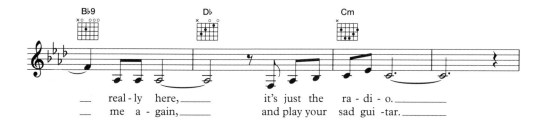

| | real - ly | here,___ | | it's just the | ra - di - o.___ |
| | me a - | gain,___ | | and play your | sad gui -tar.___ |

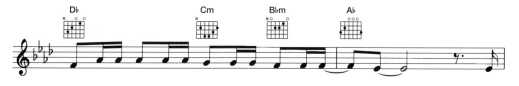

Don't you re-mem-ber you told me you loved me ba - by?___ You

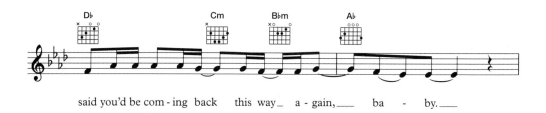

said you'd be com - ing back   this way_ a - gain,___ ba - by.___

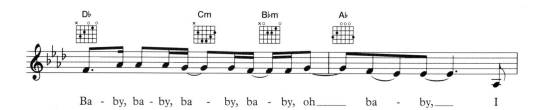

Ba - by, ba - by, ba - by, ba - by, oh___ ba - by,___ I

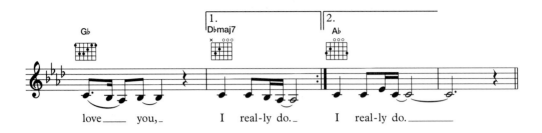

love_____ you,_ I real-ly do._ I real-ly do._____

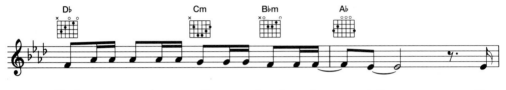

Don't you re-mem-ber you told me you loved me ba - by?___ You

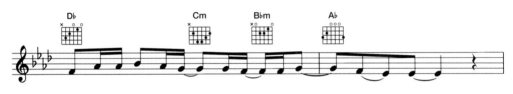

said you'd be com - ing back this way_ a - gain,___ ba - by.___

Ba - by, ba - by, ba - by, ba - by, oh_____ ba - by,___ I

love_____ you,_ I real-ly do._____

25

THERE'S A KIND OF HUSH

WORDS & MUSIC BY GEOFF STEPHENS & LES REED

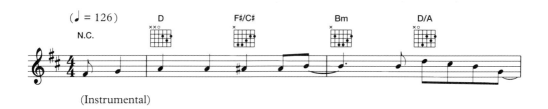

(Instrumental)

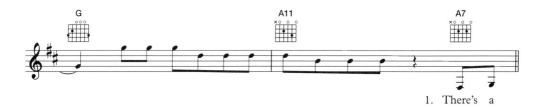

1. There's a

kind of hush___ all o - ver the world___ to - night,

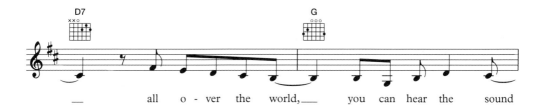

___ all o - ver the world,___ you can hear the sound

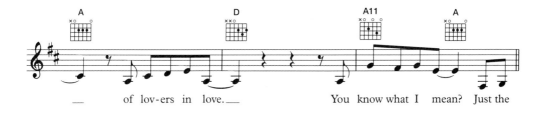

___ of lov-ers in love.___ You know what I mean? Just the

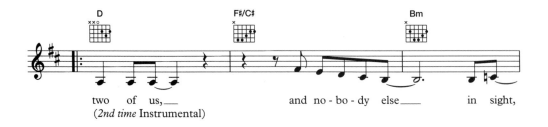

two of us,___   and no - bo - dy else___ in sight,
(2nd time Instrumental)

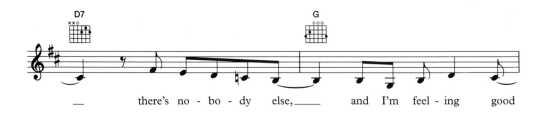

___ there's no - bo - dy else,___ and I'm feel - ing good

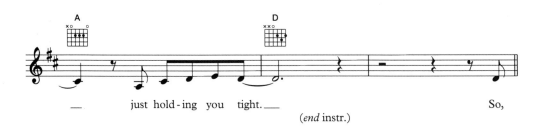

___ just hold - ing you tight.___   So,
(end instr.)

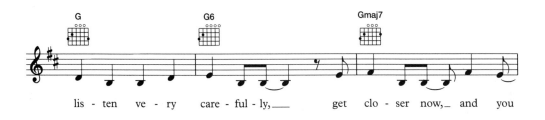

lis - ten ve - ry care - ful - ly,___ get clo - ser now,_ and you

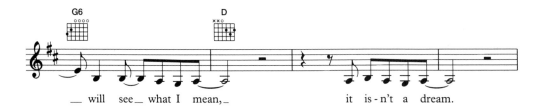

___ will see_ what I mean,_   it is - n't a dream.

The on - ly sound that you will hear,__ is

when I whis - per in__ your ear,__ 'I love you,'__

for ev - er - and ev - er._____ There's a
There's a

kind of hush__ all o - ver the world__ to - night,
kind of hush__ all o -ver the world__ to -night,

__ all o - ver the world,__ peo - ple just like us__
__ all o - ver the world,__ you can hear the sound

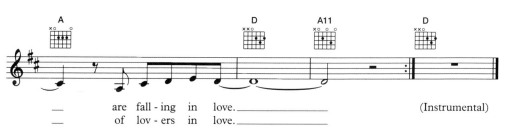

__ are fall - ing in love._____ (Instrumental)
__ of lov - ers in love._____

(THEY LONG TO BE) CLOSE TO YOU

WORDS BY HAL DAVID. MUSIC BY BURT BACHARACH
© COPYRIGHT 1963 BY U.S. SONGS INCORPORATED, USA.
CARLIN MUSIC CORPORATION, IRON BRIDGE HOUSE, 3 BRIDGE APPROACH, LONDON NW1
FOR THE UK, BRITISH COMMONWEALTH (EXCLUDING CANADA & AUSTRALASIA) EIRE AND ISRAEL.
ALL RIGHTS RESERVED. INTERNATIONAL COPYRIGHT SECURED.

(♩. = 88)

N.C.

(Instrumental)

Cadd9

1. Why do birds sud - den - ly ap -
(2.) stars fall down from the

Bsus4   B   Bm7   Em7   Em

- pear ev -ery time you are near?
— sky, — ev -ery time you walk by?

Cmaj7   Cadd9   C   Cadd9   Gadd9   Gmaj9

Just like me, they long to be close to you.
Just like me, they long to be close to you.

1.

2. Why do

2.
G9   G7   C

On the day that you were born, the

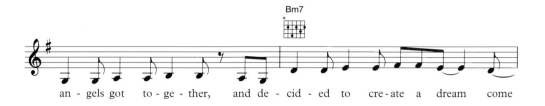

an - gels got to - ge - ther, and de - cid - ed to cre - ate a dream come

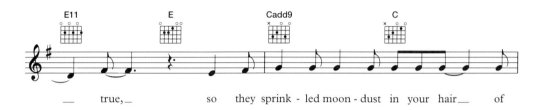

__ true, __ so they sprink - led moon - dust in your hair __ of

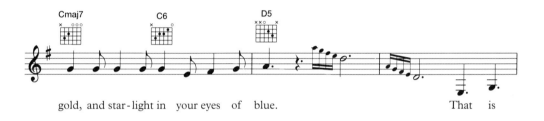

gold, and star - light in your eyes of blue. That is

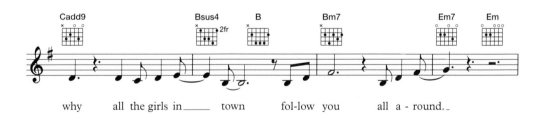

why all the girls in __ town fol - low you all a - round. __

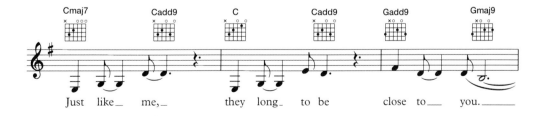

Just like __ me, __ they long __ to be close to __ you. __

(Instrumental)

On the day that you were born, the an - gels got to - ge - ther, and de -

- cid - ed to cre - ate a dream come ___ true, ___ so they

sprink - led moon-dust in your hair ___ of gold, and star - light in your eyes of

blue. That is why all the girls in town fol-low

you all a-round. Just like me, they long to be close to you.

Just like me, they long to be close to you.

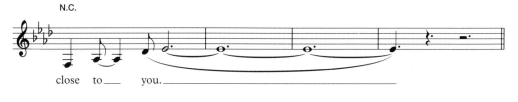

close to you.

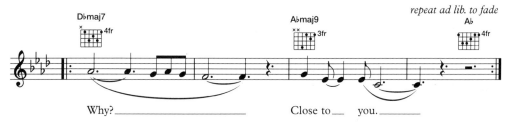

repeat ad lib. to fade

Why? Close to you.

THIS MASQUERADE

WORDS & MUSIC BY LEON RUSSELL

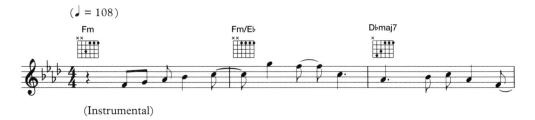

(Instrumental)

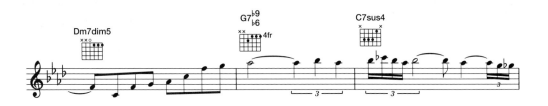

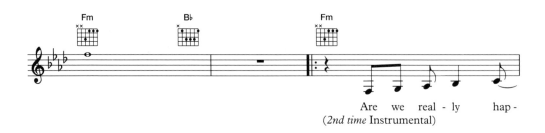

Are we real - ly hap -
(*2nd time* Instrumental)

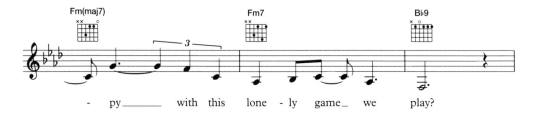

- py_____ with this lone - ly game___ we play?

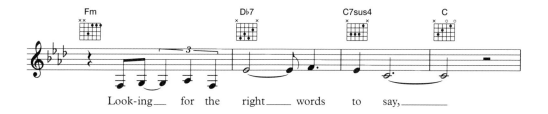

Look-ing___ for the right___ words to say,_____

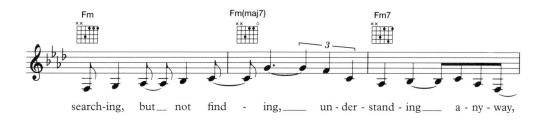

search-ing, but___ not find - ing,_____ un - der - stand - ing_____ a - ny - way,

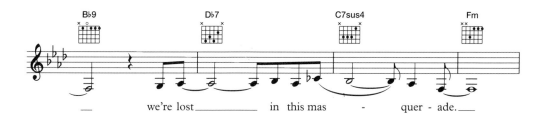

___ we're lost_____ in this mas - quer - ade.___

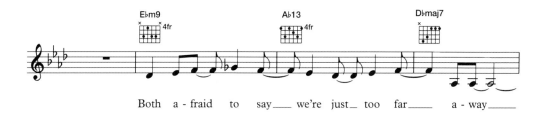

Both a - fraid to say___ we're just___ too far_____ a - way_____

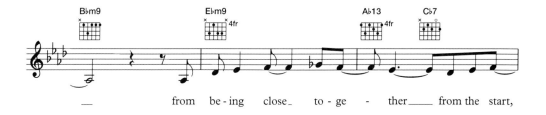

___ from be - ing close___ to - ge - ther_____ from the start,

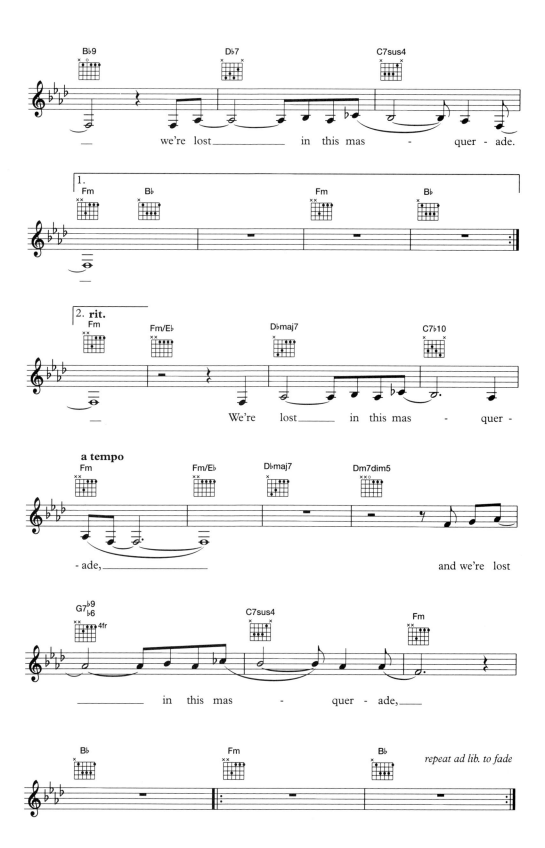

28
TICKET TO RIDE

WORDS & MUSIC BY JOHN LENNON & PAUL MCCARTNEY
© COPYRIGHT 1965 NORTHERN SONGS.

(Instrumental)

1. I think I'm gon-na be sad,_
(2.) said that liv-ing with me_

_ I think it's to-day,___ yeah,___ the
_ was bring-ing him down,___ yeah,___

boy__ that's driv-ing__ me mad___ is go-ing
he__ would ne-ver__ be free___ when I was

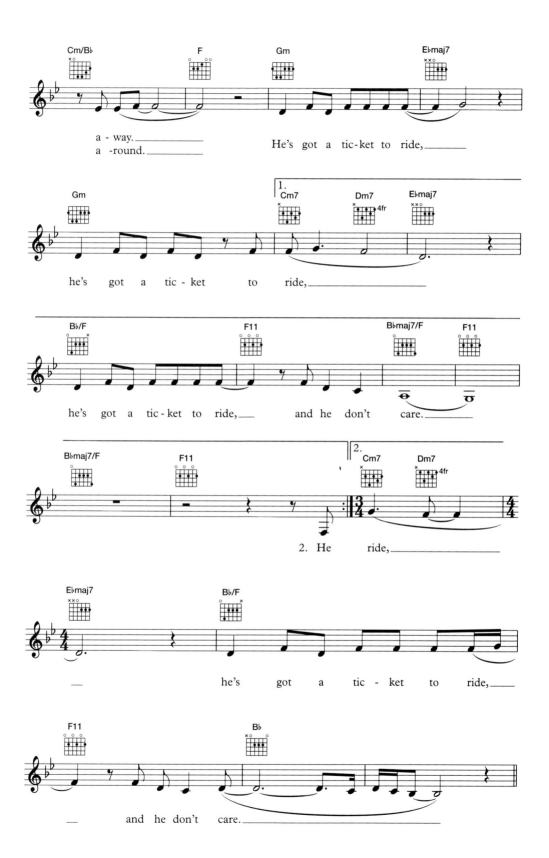

29

TOP OF THE WORLD

WORDS BY JOHN BETTIS. MUSIC BY RICHARD CARPENTER

(Instrumental)

1. Such a feel-in's com-in' o-ver me,___
2. Some-thing in___ the wind has learned my name,___

there is won-der in___ most ev-ery-thing I___ see,___
and it's tell-in' me___ that things are not___ the___ same.

not a cloud___ in the sky,___ got the sun in my
In the leaves___ on the trees,___ and the touch of the

WALK ON BY

MUSIC BY BURT BACHARACH. WORDS BY HAL DAVID

1. If you see me walk-ing down the street, and I start to cry____ each time we meet,
2. I just can't get o - ver los - ing you, and so if I seem____ bro - ken and blue,____

____ walk on by,____ walk on____ by,____
____ walk on by,____ walk on____ by,____

make be - lieve____ that you don't see the tears, just let me grieve in
fool - ish pride, that's all that I have left, so let me hide____ the

pri - vate, 'cause each time I see you, I break down and cry.
tears, and the sad - ness you gave me, when you said good - bye.

Walk on by,____ walk on by,____

repeat ad lib. to fade

walk on by.____

WE'VE ONLY JUST BEGUN

WORDS BY PAUL WILLIAMS. MUSIC BY ROGER NICHOLS

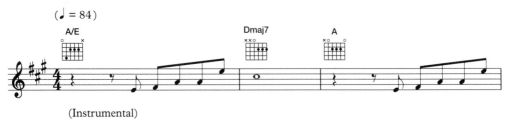

(Instrumental)

1. We've on - ly just be - gun___ to live,_____

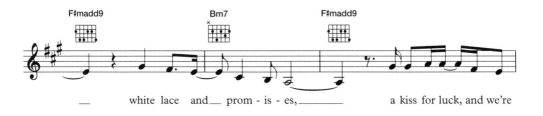

___ white lace and___ prom - is - es, _____ a kiss for luck, and we're

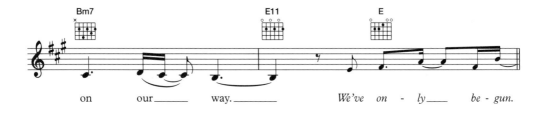

on our_____ way._____ *We've on - ly___ be - gun.*

2. Be - fore___ the ris - ing sun,_____ we___
3. And when___ the eve - ning comes,_____ we

— fly,_____ so ma - ny____ roads to choose,____
smile,_____ so much of life a - head,_____

— we start out walk - ing, and learn to_____ run,____
— we'll find a place where there's room to grow,_____

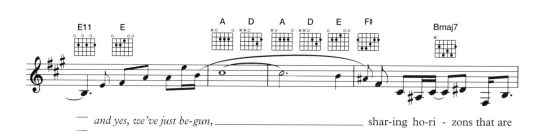

— and yes, we've just be-gun,_____ shar-ing ho-ri - zons that are

new to us, watch-ing the signs a - long the way,__

think - ing it o - ver, just the two____ of us,

32

YESTERDAY ONCE MORE

WORDS & MUSIC BY RICHARD CARPENTER & JOHN BETTIS

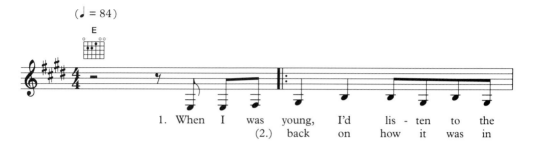

1. When I was young, I'd lis-ten to the
(2.) back on how it was in

ra-di-o,___ wait-in' for my fav-'rite songs,___ when they
years gone by,___ and the good times that I had,___ makes to-

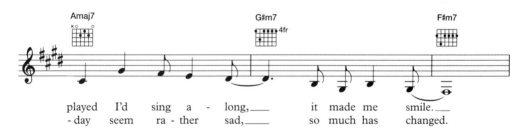

played I'd sing a-long,___ it made me smile.___
-day seem ra-ther sad,___ so much has changed.

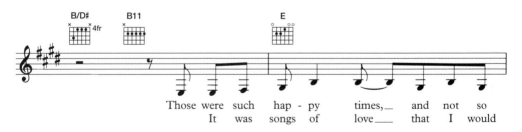

Those were such hap-py times,___ and not so
It was songs of love___ that I would

long a-go,___ how I won-dered where they'd gone,
sing to them,___ and I'd mem-or-ise each word,